151

Lenny LeBlanc & Paul Baloche
Copyright © 1999 Lensongs Publishing/
Integrity's Hosanna! Music/Sovereign Music UK

ABOVE ALL powers, above all kings,
Above all nature and all created things;
Above all wisdom and all the ways of man,
You were here before the world began.

Above all kingdoms, above all thrones,
Above all wonders the world has ever known;
Above all wealth and treasures of the earth,
There's no way to measure what You're
   worth.

Crucified, laid behind the stone;
You lived to die, rejected and alone;
Like a rose trampled on the ground,
You took the fall and thought of me,
Above all.

152

Dave Bilbrough
Copyright © 2002 Thankyou Music

AGAIN AND AGAIN,
You have revealed Your love to me.
Again and again grace has shone through.
You've always been there for me
When I have come to You:
You are the Rock on which I stand.

You're wonderful, You're marvellous,
You're everything to me.
Your steadfast and unchanging love
Are all I'll ever need.
What peace and what security
Can be found in knowing You,
My Healer, Deliverer.

There is no limit to this never-ending stream
That's entered the castle of my soul.
You give me a hope and future
Beyond my wildest dreams.
Your love is greater than I know.

You've been my fortress
Through the shifting sands of time;
In change and adversity
You have answered my prayer to guide me.

11

A HU...
And ...
If the ...
Let a...
If Yo...
I'm gonna be right here tomorrow.
If You don't answer when I pray
From the morning to the evening,
'Cause it's You I do believe in,
I will say, every day, I'm gonna say that...

I won't let go till You bless me, Lord,
No, I won't let go till You bless me, Lord.
And I will cry out to You
Till I can't cry no more.
And I won't let go till You bless me, Lord.

Where can I go if You don't bid me go?
And I have no hope if You are not my hope.
And I have no peace if You don't give me
   peace,
And I have no faith if You don't help me to
   believe.
If You don't answer me today
Will the heathen nations mock Your name
And say You're made of wood or clay?
Ah, but I've seen You provide for me,
I've kissed Your lips and felt You heal my
   pain.
Hey, can You do it once again? 'Cause...

1154

Paul Oakley
Copyright © 1999 Thankyou Music

ALL AROUND YOUR THRONE,
Rainbow colours fly through light,
And heavy thunder rolls,
And the lightning blinds, so bright.
Living creatures cry "Holy is the Lord,"
As they try to hide their eyes.

Rulers of this world
Only join in vain as one.
There's no other power
Could ever overthrow Your Son.
Principalities and powers
Know that You are Lord,
And they try to hide their eyes.

'Cause You shine brighter than the sun,
Only Holy One,
And You shine on me,
Oh, Jesus, only risen Son,
Seated on Your throne,
Would You shine on me today?

There will be a day
When the stars will leave the sky,
Heaven and earth will shake,
And the moon will give no light;
While every tongue will cry
"Jesus Christ is Lord,"
Some will try to hide their eyes.

1155 Marty Sampson
Copyright © 2001 Marty Sampson/
Hillsong Publishing/Kingsway Music

ALL CREATION CRIES TO YOU,
Worshipping in spirit and in truth.
Glory to the Faithful One,
Jesus Christ, God's Son.

All creation gives You praise,
You alone are truly great;
You alone are God who reigns
For eternity.

God is great and His praise
Fills the earth, fills the heavens,
And Your name will be praised
Through all the world.
God is great, sing His praise
All the earth, all the heavens,
'Cause we're living for the glory of Your
name,
The glory of Your name.

All to You, O God, we bring.
Jesus, teach us how to live.
Let Your fire burn in us
That all may hear and all may see.

"Holy is the Lord,"
The whole earth sings,
The whole earth sings.
(Repeat)

1156 Tony Ryce-Kelly & Rónán Johnston
Copyright © 1997 Emmausongs/
Adm. by Daybreak Music Ltd

ALLELUIA, ALLELUIA, Jesus is the Lord,
He's the Lord of all my heart.
Alleluia, alleluia, Jesus is the Lord,
He's the Lord of all my heart.

He's the way, He's the truth, He's the life. *(×3)*
(Last time)
You're the way, You're the truth, You're the
light.

1157 Theodulph of Orleans (c.750–821)
Tr. John Mason Neale (1818–66)

ALL GLORY, LAUD AND HONOUR
To Thee, Redeemer, King,
To whom the lips of children
Made sweet hosannas ring.
Thou art the King of Israel,
Thou David's royal Son,
Who in the Lord's name comest,
The King and blessèd One.

The company of angels
Are praising Thee on high,
And mortal men and all things
Created make reply.
The people of the Hebrews
With psalms before Thee went;
Our praise and prayer and anthems
Before Thee we present.

To Thee before Thy passion
They sang their hymns of praise;
To Thee now high exalted
Our melody we raise.
Thou didst accept their praises;
Accept the prayers we bring,
Who in all good delightest,
Thou good and gracious King.

All glory, laud and honour
To Thee, Redeemer, King,
To whom the lips of children
Made sweet hosannas ring.

1158 Stuart Townend
Copyright © 1998 Thankyou Music

ALL MY DAYS I will sing this song of
gladness,
Give my praise to the Fountain of delights;
For in my helplessness You heard my cry,
And waves of mercy poured down on my li

I will trust in the cross of my Redeemer,
I will sing of the blood that never fails;
Of sins forgiven, of conscience cleansed,
Of death defeated and life without end.

Beautiful Saviour, Wonderful Counsello
Clothed in majesty, Lord of history,
You're the Way, the Truth, the Life.
Star of the Morning, glorious in holines
You're the Risen One, heaven's Champi
And You reign, You reign over all!

I long to be where the praise is never-endin
Yearn to dwell where the glory never fades
Where countless worshippers will share on
song,
And cries of 'worthy' will honour the Lamb

159 Liz Holland
Copyright © 1999 Thankyou Music

ALL MY LIFE, all my will, every day,
lay it all before You.
All my life, all my will, every day,
lay it all before You now.

And Jesus takes us to the place of true
*   surrender,*
Where we become less and You become
*   greater;*
And Your holy ways into our lives will
*   enter,*
And all that we are, and all that we have
*   become Yours.*

All my pain, all the fears, every tear,
lay them all before You.
All my pain, all the fears, every tear,
lay them all before You now.

160 Gareth Robinson
Copyright © 2001 Thankyou Music

ALL OF ME,
All of me I give to You,
only You, Jesus.
More of You,
More of You I long for,
only You, Jesus.

For this life I live for You;
truly worship You.
All of my days, in every way,
will praise You.
In thought and word and deed,
powered by Your life in me,
all of my days, in every way,
will praise You, Lord.

161 Chris Tomlin & Louie Giglio
Copyright © 2002 worshiptogether.com songs/
Six Steps Music/Adm. by Kingsway Music

ALL OF YOU *is more than enough for*
All of me, for every thirst and every need,
You satisfy me with Your love,
And all I have in You
Is more than enough.

You're my supply,
my breath of life;
Still more awesome than I know.
You're my reward,
worth living for;
Still more awesome than I know.

You're my sacrifice
Of greatest price;
Still more awesome than I know.
You're my coming King,
You are everything;
Still more awesome than I know.

More than all I want,
More than all I need,
You are more than enough for me.
More than all I know,
More than all I can,
You are more than enough.

1162 Fanny Crosby (1820–1915)

ALL THE WAY MY SAVIOUR LEADS ME,
What have I to ask beside?
Can I doubt His tender mercy,
Who through life has been my guide?
Heavenly peace, divinest comfort,
Here by faith in Him to dwell,
For I know whate'er befall me,
Jesus doeth all things well.

All the way my Saviour leads me,
Cheers each winding path I tread.
Gives me grace for every trial,
Feeds me with the Living Bread.
Though my weary steps may falter
And my soul athirst may be,
Gushing from a Rock before me,
Lo! a spring of joy I see.

And all the way my Saviour leads me,
Oh, the fullness of His love.
Perfect rest to me is promised
In my Father's house above.
And when my spirit clothed immortal
Wings its flight to realms of day,
This my song through endless ages,
Jesus led me all the way.

1163 J.W. van de Venter (1855–1939)
Copyright © HarperCollins Religious/
Adm. by CopyCare

ALL TO JESUS I SURRENDER,
All to Him I freely give;
I will ever love and trust Him,
In His presence daily live.

I surrender all,
I surrender all,
All to Thee, my blessèd Saviour,
I surrender all.

All to Jesus I surrender,
Humbly at His feet I bow;
Worldly pleasures all forsaken,
Take me, Jesus, take me now.

All to Jesus I surrender,
Make me, Saviour, wholly Thine;
Let me feel the Holy Spirit,
Truly know that Thou art mine.

All to Jesus I surrender,
Lord, I give myself to Thee;
Fill me with Thy love and power,
Let Thy blessing fall on me.

All to Jesus I surrender,
Now I feel the sacred flame;
O the joy of full salvation!
Glory, glory to His name!

1164

ALL WHO ARE THIRSTY,
All who are weak,
Come to the fountain,
Dip your heart in the stream of life.
Let the pain and the sorrow
Be washed away
In the waves of His mercy,
As deep cries out to deep.
(We sing)

Come, Lord Jesus, come. *(×4)*

Holy Spirit come. *(×3)*

1165

ALMIGHTY GOD, faithful and true,
In my worship I want to meet with You.
Unchanging God, for ever the same,
It's You I worship,
To know Your heart again.

And I fall down on my knees again,
As You show me what grace means;
And You love with such amazing love,
O my God, how can this be?

1166

ALMIGHTY GOD, HOLY ONE,
Who can stand before You,
Who can come?
Perfect Lamb, who bore our sin,
Who deserves such mercy,
Gracious King?

I come to Your throne of grace,
I'm standing in Christ,
I'm clothed in His righteousness.
To know Your presence,
To seek Your face.
Father, I delight in Your embrace.

1167

ALMIGHTY GOD,
TO WHOM ALL HEARTS ARE OPEN,
All desires known,
And from whom no secrets are hidden:
Cleanse the thoughts of our hearts
By the inspiration of Your Holy Spirit,
That we may perfectly love You,
And worthily magnify,
That we may perfectly love You,
And worthily magnify
Your holy name;
Through Christ our Lord,
Amen.
Through Christ our Lord,
Amen.

1168

AMAZING GRACE, how sweet the sound
That saved a wretch like me;
I once was lost, but now am found,
Was blind, but now I see.

Amazing love has come to me.
I lift up my voice to the heavens,
Lift up my hands to the King,
And I cry 'hosanna, hosanna in the
*   highest.'*
Jesus my Lord is exalted
Far above every name,
And I cry 'hosanna, hosanna in the
*   highest.'*

'Twas grace that taught my heart to fear,
And grace my fears relieved;
How precious did that grace appear,
The hour I first believed!

The Lord has promised good to me,
His word my hope secures;
He will my shield and portion be
As long as life endures.

AND AFTER ALL,
everything I once held dear
Just proved to be so vain.
To lose it all,
And find a Friend who's always near
Could only be my gain.
And when I think of what You've done for me,
To bring me to the Father's side:

Unashamed and unafraid,
I will choose to wear Your name,
In a world so full of hate,
I will always live Your way.

Could it be
That You should put on human flesh,
Your glory laid aside?
Bruised for me,
Majesty upon the cross,
Forsaken and despised.
When I think of what it cost for You,
To bring me to the Father's side:

Unashamed and unafraid,
I will choose to wear Your name,
In a world so full of hate,
I will always live Your way.
Unashamed and unafraid,
I will love You all my days,
I don't care what people say,
I'm unashamed and unafraid.

I know some will say it's foolishness:
You can't make a blind man see.
But I know that there is power in the cross
To save those who believe.

AND I'M FORGIVEN, because You were
forsaken.
And I'm accepted: You were condemned.
And I'm alive and well,
Your Spirit is within me,
Because You died and rose again.

Amazing love, how can it be
That You, my King, would die for me?
Amazing love, I know it's true;
Now it's my joy to honour You.
In all I do, I honour You.

You are my King, You are my King,
Jesus, You are my King,
You are my King.

ANGELS BOW before You,
Kings fall at Your command.
And yet Your love comes down to earth
To fallen man.
How can I know Your workings,
Eternal mystery?
I must bow down and give my life,
Must follow You.

And I love You, Lord,
Everything belongs to You,
Is known by You,
And made for Your eternal glory.
You, my Lord, receive the praise
Of my thankful heart.

A REFUGE FOR THE POOR,
A shelter from the storm:
This is our God.
He will wipe away your tears
And return your wasted years:
This is our God.

Oh, mmm, this is our God.
Oh, mmm, this is our God.

A Father to the orphan,
A healer to the broken:
This is our God.
He brings peace to our madness
And comfort in our sadness:
This is our God.

A fountain for the thirsty,
A lover for the lonely:
This is our God.
He brings glory to the humble
And crowns for the faithful:
This is our God.

This is the One we have waited for,
This is the One we have waited for,
This is the One we have waited for.

ARE THE PRAYERS OF THE SAINTS
Like sweet smelling incense,
Are the prayers of the saints
Like sweet smelling incense to Your heart,
To Your heart?
(Repeat)

Let these prayers of the saints
Be sweet smelling incense,
Let these prayers of the saints
Be sweet smelling incense to Your heart.

Are the songs of the saints
Like sweet smelling incense,
Are the songs of the saints
Like sweet smelling incense to Your heart,
To your heart?
(Repeat)

Let these songs of the saints
Be sweet smelling incense,
Let these songs of the saints
Be sweet smelling incense to Your heart.

1174
Steve & Vikki Cook
Copyright © 1999 PDI Worship/
Adm. by CopyCare

AROUND YOU SUCH BEAUTY,
Your majesty could fill an endless sky:
Holy are You, Lord.
Transcendent, exalted,
The heavens cannot contain Your presence:
Holy are You, Lord.
And as I behold Your glory
I'm undone.

I bow down at Your feet,
I bow down at Your feet,
I bow down at Your feet
For You are my God, my God.

You saved me, the sinner,
With crimson red You washed me white as
snow:
How I love You, Lord.
You loved me, the mocker,
With kindness You won my heart for ever:
How I love You, Lord.
And as I behold this mercy
I'm undone.

1175
Jim Bailey
Copyright © 1997 Thankyou Music

AS FOR ME AND MY HOUSE,
As for me and my family,
As for me and my children,
We will serve the Lord.
(Repeat)

In this family,
We're gonna do things properly,
Read God's word every day
And then we'll try to pray;
Although we get it wrong,
We will still carry on,
Make Jesus number one in this place.
In this place we're gonna say grace.

1176
Robin Mark
Copyright © 1998 Daybreak Music Ltd

AS SURE AS GOLD IS PRECIOUS and the
honey sweet,
So You love this city and You love these
streets.
Every child out playing by their own front
door;
Every baby lying on the bedroom floor.

Every dreamer dreaming in her dead-end jo
Every driver driving through the rush hour
mob.
I feel it in my spirit, feel it in my bones,
You're going to send revival,
Bring them all back home.

I can hear that thunder in the distance,
Like a train on the edge of the town;
I can feel the brooding of Your Spirit:
'Lay your burdens down, lay your burde
down.'

From the preacher preaching when the wel
is dry,
To the lost soul reaching for a higher high.
From the young man working through his
hopes and fears,
To the widow walking through the vale of
tears.

Every man and woman, every old and youn
Every father's daughter, every mother's son
I feel it in my spirit, feel it in my bones,
You're going to send revival,
Bring them all back home.

I can hear...

Revive us, revive us,
Revive us with Your fire!
(Repeat)

1177
Graham Kendrick
Copyright © 2002 Make Way Music

AS WE BRING OUR SONGS of love today,
Do you hear a sound more glorious?
Like the mighty roar of ocean waves,
Many witnesses surround us.
It's a harmony of costly praise
From the lips of those who suffer,
Of sighs and tears and martyrs' prayers
Until this age is over.

How long, Lord, till You come?
How long till the earth
Is filled with Your song?
How long until Your justice
Shines like the sun?
How long, Lord, till You come?
How long till the earth
Is filled with Your song?
How long? How long?

ɔrd, help us to live worthy of
ᵘr sisters and our brothers
⅃ho love You more than their own lives,
⅃ho worship as they suffer:
ɔ embrace the scandal of the cross.
lot ashamed to tell Your story,
ɔ count all earthly gain as loss,
ɔ know You and Your glory.

How long, Lord, till You come?
How long till the earth
Is filled with Your song?
How long until Your justice
Shines like the sun?
How long, Lord, till You come?
How long till the whole world hears
And the work is done,
Until at last we see You return?
How long, Lord, till You come?
How long till the earth
Is filled with Your song?
How long? How long?

178   Matt Redman
Copyright © 2000 Thankyou Music

S WE COME TODAY,
⅃e remind ourselves of what we do;
ʰat these songs are not just songs,
ᵘt signs of love for You.
ʰis is a holy moment now,
ɔmething of heaven touches earth,
ɔices of angels all resound,
⅃e join their song.

Come, come, come, let us worship God
With our hands held high,
And our hearts bowed down.
We will run, run, run
Through Your gates, O God,
With a shout of love,
With a shout of love.

Lord, with confidence
We come before Your throne of grace.
Not that we deserve to come
But You have paid the way.
You are the holy King of all,
Heaven and earth are in Your hands,
All of the angels sing Your song,
We join them now.

Let this be a holy moment now. *(Repeat)*

1179   Paul Baloche
Copyright © 1996 Integrity's Hosanna! Music/
Sovereign Music UK

AS WE LIFT UP YOUR NAME, *(Leader – echo)*
Let Your fire fall.
Send Your wind and rain,
On Your wings of love.
Pour out from heaven *(All)*
Your passion and presence,
Bring down Your burning desire.

Revival fire, fall!
Revival fire, fall!
Fall on us here
In the power of Your Spirit;
Father, let revival fire fall.
Revival fire, fall!
Revival fire, fall!
Let the flame consume us
With hearts ablaze for Jesus;
Father, let revival fire fall!

As we lift up Your name, *(Leader – echo)*
Let Your kingdom come,
Have Your way in this place,
Let Your will be done.
Pour out from heaven *(All)*
Your passion and presence,
Bring down Your burning desire.

1180   Tré Sheppard
Copyright © 2002 Thankyou Music

AT THE FOOT OF THE CROSS
Where I kneel in adoration,
And I lay my burdens down
I exchange all my sin
For the promise of salvation,
And Your name across my brow.

At the foot of the cross
I give up my vain ambition,
And I leave my selfish pride.
In the peace that is there
Will You restore my vision
In all the places I am blind?

I will wait here at the cross. (×4)

At the foot of the cross
There is healing for this nation,
There is rest for those who wait;
And the love that we find
Is the hope of all creation,
We are stunned by what You gave.

We will wait here at the cross. (×4)

We will wait at the cross,
A hungry generation,
With our broken hearts and lives.
Will You hear, will You come,
Will You fill our desperation?
O God, let this be the time.

We will wait here at the cross. (×4)

1181 Martin E. Leckebusch
Copyright © 2000 Kevin Mayhew Ltd

AT THIS TABLE WE REMEMBER
How and where our faith began:
In the pain of crucifixion
Suffered by the Son of Man.

Looking up in adoration
Faith is conscious – He is here!
Christ is present with His people,
His the call that draws us near.

Heart and mind we each examine:
If with honesty we face
All our doubt, our fear and failure,
Then we can receive His grace.

Peace we share with one another:
As from face to face we turn
In our brothers and our sisters
Jesus' body we discern.

Bread and wine are set before us;
As we eat, we look ahead:
We shall dine with Christ in heaven
Where the kingdom feast is spread.

Nourished by the bread of heaven,
Faith and strength and courage grow –
So to witness, serve and suffer,
Out into the world we go.

1182 Nathan Fellingham
Copyright © 1999 Thankyou Music

AWAKE, AWAKE, O ZION,
And clothe yourself with strength,
Shake off your dust
And fix your eyes on Him.
For you have been redeemed by
The precious blood of Jesus,
And now you sit enthroned with Him.

*Our God reigns,
He is King of all the earth.
Our God reigns,
And He's seated on the throne.
Lift your voice,
And sing a song of praise.
Our God reigns,
The awesome Lord most high.*

How beautiful the feet are
Of those who bring good news,
For they proclaim the peace that comes fro
   God.
Rise up, you holy nation,
Proclaim the great salvation,
And say to Zion 'Your God reigns.'

Emmanuel, Emmanuel,
Our God is with us now.

The watchmen lift their voices,
And raise a shout of joy,
For He will come again.
Then all eyes will see the
Salvation of our God,
For He has redeemed Jerusalem.

1183 Owen Hurter
Copyright © 2001 Thankyou Music

AWAKE, MY SOUL, rise up from your
   sleeping;
Do not slumber or sleep any more.
Raise your weary head to a new day;
Lift your shout, let your voice be heard.

Rocks will cry out if we are silent,
Trees will clap their hands and rejoice;
The mighty ocean roars with a new song,
Mountains bow down to honour Your name

*Rise up, my soul, and sing.
Rise up, my soul, and sing.
Rise up, my soul, and give glory to the
   Lord.*
(Repeat)

Let the song of a bride in blooming
Thunder clap through the heavens above.
Rising up in true adoration,
Arise and shine for Your light has come.

I don't want to sleep any more,
But I'll awake the dawn with singing.
Hear this crying heart of mine,
As I lift up my song.
(Repeat)

Lift it up, lift it up, lift it up.

1184

Darlene Zschech
Copyright © 1997 Darlene Zschech/
Hillsong Publishing/Kingsway Music

BEAUTIFUL LORD, wonderful Saviour,
I know for sure, all of my days are
Held in Your hand,
Crafted into Your perfect plan.
You gently call me into Your presence,
Guiding me by Your Holy Spirit.
Teach me, dear Lord, to live all of my life
Through Your eyes.

I'm captured by Your holy calling,
Set me apart.
I know You're drawing me to Yourself;
Lead me, Lord, I pray.

Take me, mould me, use me, fill me;
I give my life to the Potter's hand.
Call me, guide me, lead me, walk beside me;
I give my life to the Potter's hand.

1185

Dave Bilbrough
Copyright © 1999 Thankyou Music

BECAUSE OF YOU, I can be free;
Because of You, I can be me.
Since that day when love broke through,
My life was changed because of You.

You fill my heart with melody,
Salvation is my song.
The way was opened up for me
To know You as my God.

So I will sing for joy, sing for joy,
Sing for joy to You.
Yes, I will sing for joy, sing for joy,
Sing for joy to You.
(Repeat)

1186

Lara Martin (Abundant Life Ministries,
Bradford, England)
Copyright © 2002 Thankyou Music

BEFORE ONE EVER CAME TO BE,
All the days ordained for me
Were written in Your book of days.
You are the One who fashioned me,
The One I praise continually,
So perfect are Your ways.
I will rejoice and be glad.
And in all things I give thanks.

This is the day You have made,
I will rejoice, I will rejoice:
In You I boast. (in my God)
This is the day You have made,
I will rejoice, I will rejoice:
In You I boast.

1187

Charitie L. Bancroft (1841–92)

BEFORE THE THRONE OF GOD ABOVE,
I have a strong, a perfect plea,
A great High Priest whose name is Love,
Who ever lives and pleads for me.
My name is graven on His hands,
My name is written on His heart;
I know that while in heaven He stands
No tongue can bid me thence depart,
No tongue can bid me thence depart.

When Satan tempts me to despair,
And tells me of the guilt within,
Upward I look and see Him there
Who made an end to all my sin.
Because the sinless Saviour died,
My sinful soul is counted free;
For God the Just is satisfied
To look on Him and pardon me,
To look on Him and pardon me.

Behold Him there! The risen Lamb,
My perfect, spotless righteousness;
The great unchangeable I AM,
The King of glory and of grace!
One with Himself I cannot die,
My soul is purchased with His blood;
My life is hid with Christ on high,
With Christ, my Saviour and my God,
With Christ my Saviour and my God.

1188

Matt Redman
Copyright © 2002 Thankyou Music

BEFRIENDED,
Befriended by the King above all kings.
Surrendered,
Surrendered to the Friend above all friends.

Invited,
Invited deep into this mystery.
Delighted,
Delighted by the wonders I have seen.

This will be my story,
This will be my song:
You'll always be my Saviour,
Jesus, You will always have my heart.

Astounded,
Astounded that Your gospel beckoned me.
Surrounded,
Surrounded, but I've never been so free.

Determined,
Determined now to live this life for You.
You're so worthy,
My greatest gift would be the least You're
  due.

1189 Robert Critchley
Copyright © 1996 Thankyou Music

BEHOLD THE LAMB OF GLORY COMES,
In majesty He rides.
Behold the Lion of Judah comes,
In majesty He rides.

He rides in majesty, majesty He rides.
He rides in majesty, majesty He rides.

Behold the Sun of Righteousness,
On a white horse He rides.
His cavalry is following Him,
An army from on high.

And when the Lord goes to battle,
Who can stand against His awesome might?

Let God arise
And His enemies be scattered.
Whoa, whoa.
(Repeat)

The watchmen on the tower
Are interceding for the land.
The saints proclaim God's victory,
He stretches forth His hand.

1190 Paul Oakley
Copyright © 2001 Thankyou Music

BE LIFTED UP, be lifted up.
As we bow down,
Be lifted up.
(Repeat)

Let the heavens rejoice,
Let the nations be glad.
Let the whole earth tremble,
For You are God.
Come and worship the Lord
In the beauty of holiness.

As we bow down,
Be lifted up.
(Repeat)

1191 Stuart Townend
Copyright © 2000 Thankyou Music

BELOVÈD AND BLESSÈD,
The Father's pure delight.
Redeemer, Sustainer,
You're my passion and my prize.

My Brother, my Comforter,
My Shepherd and my Friend.
My Ransom, my Righteousness,
You're the Stream that never ends.

You're unchanging, You're magnificent,
You are all I could desire.
You're my Breath of life,
Sun of righteousness,
You're the Love that satisfies.

There's kindness, compassion
For those who will draw near;
Acceptance, forgiveness,
And a love that conquers fear.

You're the Word of life,
You're the Bread of heaven,
You're the Lion and the Lamb.
All within me cries,
'Lord be glorified
By everything I am.'

Belovèd, my Belovèd.

1192 David Lyle Morris & Pat Youd
Copyright © 2000 Thankyou Music

BLESSÈD ARE THE POOR in spirit,
For theirs is the kingdom of heaven.
Blessèd are the mourning hearts,
Comfort to them will be given.
Blessèd are the humble and meek,
They will inherit the earth.
Blessèd are those who hunger and thirst
For righteousness,
For they will be filled.

Rejoice and be glad,
For great your reward in heaven.
(Repeat)

Blessèd are the merciful,
For mercy to them will be shown.
Blessèd are the pure in heart,
For they will see their God.
Blessèd are the makers of peace,
They will be called sons of God.
Blessèd are those who suffer for Christ
And righteousness,
Theirs is the kingdom of heaven.

Give glory to God,
For He's our reward in heaven.
(Repeat)

Rejoice and be glad,
Give glory to God in heaven.
(Repeat)

1193

Matt & Beth Redman
Copyright © 2002 Thankyou Music

BLESSÈD BE YOUR NAME
In the land that is plentiful,
Where Your streams of abundance flow,
Blessèd be Your name.
And blessèd be Your name
When I'm found in the desert place,
Though I walk through the wilderness,
Blessèd be Your name.

Every blessing You pour out I'll
turn back to praise.
When the darkness closes in, Lord,
Still I will say:

Blessèd be the name of the Lord,
Blessèd be Your name.
Blessèd be the name of the Lord,
Blessèd be Your glorious name.

Blessèd be Your name
When the sun's shining down on me,
When the world's 'all as it should be',
Blessèd be Your name.
And blessèd be Your name
On the road marked with suffering,
Though there's pain in the offering,
Blessèd be Your name.

You give and take away,
You give and take away,
My heart will choose to say:
Lord, blessèd be Your name.

1194

Geoffrey Ainger
Copyright © 1964 Stainer & Bell Ltd

BORN IN THE NIGHT, Mary's child,
A long way from Your home;
Coming in need, Mary's child,
Born in a borrowed room.

Clear shining light, Mary's child,
Your face lights up our way:
Light of the world, Mary's child,
Dawn on our darkened day.

Truth of our life, Mary's child,
You tell us God is good:
Prove it is true, Mary's child,
Go to Your cross of wood.

Hope of the world, Mary's child,
You're coming soon to reign:
King of the earth, Mary's child,
Walk in our streets again.

1195

Andrea Lawrence & Noel Robinson
Copyright © 2000 Thankyou Music

BREATHE ON ME, O wind of change,
Anoint me with fresh oil from Your throne.
Lord, restore me with new life,
So I'm ready to serve
And I'm ready to go,
Ready to do Your will.
So I'm ready to serve
And I'm ready to go,
Ready to do Your will.

Lord, help me to run this race
And to live by Your grace,
All I want to do is Your will.
(Repeat)

Ready to serve, ready to go,
Ready to do, ready to be,
Ready to do Your will.
(Repeat)

1196

John L. Bell
Copyright © 1998 WGRG, Iona Community

BRING YOUR BEST TO THEIR WORST, *(All)*
Bring Your peace to their pain,
God of love, heal Your people.

That none who cry aloud may cry in vain:
(Leader)

That those who fear may never walk alone:

That those near death may see the light of
day:

That guilty folk may find themselves forgiven:

That those who doubt may find a deeper
faith:

That broken folk may know they will be
whole:

1197

Noel Richards & Wayne Drain
Copyright © 1998 Thankyou Music

CALLING ALL NATIONS, *hear the story*
Of God's amazing grace.
Calling all nations, come and worship,
Fill the earth with praise.

Every woman, every man,
Rich and poor, old and young,
Heaven's love is coming down
To wipe all your tears away.

There's a bell to be rung,
There's a song to be sung.
Sweeter music yet to play
When we gather on that day.

1198 Evan Rogers
Copyright © 2000 Thankyou Music

CELEBRATE IN THE LORD,
He is the reason we rejoice;
For He has cast our sins away,
Forgotten now, for ever and always,
Always, always, yes, always,
Always, always.

This is our jubilee,
No debt, no bondage, we are free.
We're free to give Him everything
For we have nothing, now it is all His,
All His, all His, it's all His,
All His, all His.

This is where the party is,
This is where the joy of heaven abounds.
In His presence we are free
To praise, to shout aloud.
This is where the party is,
Singing with the angels, hear the sound.
This is where the party is,
We are dancing on holy ground,
Holy ground, holy ground, holy ground,
Holy ground, holy ground.

For freedom You have set us free,
No longer bound to slavery,
You've broken every chain that binds;
You've conquered sin for ever and all time.
All time, all time, yes, all time,
All time, all time.

Siyavuya, siyavuya, siyavuya. (Repeat)
Jabulani, jabulani, jabulani. (Repeat)

1199 From the Latin, J.M. Neale (1818–66)
Copyright © in this version Jubilate Hymns

CHRIST IS MADE THE SURE FOUNDATION,
Christ the Head and Cornerstone,
Chosen of the Lord and precious,
Binding all the church in one;
Holy Zion's help for ever,
And her confidence alone.

All within that holy city
Dearly loved of God on high,
In exultant jubilation
Sing, in perfect harmony;
God the One-in-Three adoring
In glad hymns eternally.

We as living stones invoke You:
Come among us, Lord, today!
With Your gracious loving-kindness
Hear Your children as we pray;
And the fullness of Your blessing
In our fellowship display.

Here entrust to all Your servants
What we long from You to gain –
That on earth and in the heavens
We one people shall remain,
Till united in Your glory
Evermore with You we reign.

Praise and honour to the Father,
Praise and honour to the Son,
Praise and honour to the Spirit,
Ever Three and ever One:
One in power and one in glory
While eternal ages run.

1200 Charles Wesley (1707–88)

CHRIST, WHOSE GLORY FILLS THE SKIES,
Christ, the true, the only light,
Sun of righteousness, arise,
Triumph o'er the shades of night:
Day-spring from on high, be near;
Day-star in my heart appear.

Dark and cheerless is the morn
Unaccompanied by Thee;
Joyless is the day's return,
Till Thy mercy's beams I see;
Till they inward light impart,
Glad my eyes, and warm my heart.

Visit then this soul of mine;
Pierce the gloom of sin and grief;
Fill me, radiancy divine;
Scatter all my unbelief;
More and more Thyself display,
Shining to the perfect day.

1201 Alexander Gondo
Copyright © World Council of Churches

COME ALL YOU PEOPLE, }
Come and praise your Maker. } *(×3)*
Come now and worship the Lord.

Uyai mose, tinamate Mwari, *(×3)*
Uyai mose zvino.

1202 after Bianco da Siena (1367–1434)
Richard F. Littledale (1833–90)

COME DOWN, O LOVE DIVINE,
Seek Thou this soul of mine
And visit it with Thine own ardour glowing;
O Comforter, draw near,
Within my heart appear,
And kindle it, Thy holy flame bestowing.

O let it freely burn,
Till earthly passions turn
To dust and ashes, in its heat consuming;
And let Thy glorious light
Shine ever on my sight,
And clothe me round, the while my path
　illuming.

Let holy charity
Mine outward vesture be,
And lowliness become mine inner clothing;
True lowliness of heart,
Which takes the humbler part,
And o'er its own shortcomings weeps with
　loathing.

And so the yearning strong,
With which the soul will long,
Shall far outpass the power of human telling;
For none can guess its grace,
Till he become the place
Wherein the Holy Spirit makes His dwelling.

1203 Nathan Fellingham
Copyright © 2001 Thankyou Music

COME, LET US WORSHIP the King of kings,
The Creator of all things.
Let your soul arise to Him,
Come and bless the Lord our King.

Lord, my heart and voice I raise,
To praise Your wondrous ways,
And with confidence I come
To approach Your heavenly throne.

Come and fill this place with Your glory,
Come and captivate our gaze;
Come and fill us with Your fire,
That the world might know Your name.

(For) You are God,
And You're worthy to be praised,
And You are good,
For Your love will never end:
The great I Am,
You are faithful in all of Your ways.
(Repeat)

1204 Alan Rose
Copyright © 1998 Thankyou Music

COME NEAR TO ME, as I come near to You;
Pour out Your mercy and Your grace.
I need Your love, I need Your tenderness;
I'm longing for Your sweet embrace.

My heart cries out for more of You, Lord;
I'm so hungry for Your presence.
Your love is water to my soul.
I will be satisfied with You, Lord;
You fulfil my deepest longing.
Pour out Your Spirit once again.

Draw close to me, as I draw close to You.
Release Your power from above.
I'm dry and thirsty, Lord, come and fill me up;
I'm waiting for Your touch of love.

I've felt Your presence, Lord,
I've tasted of Your love.
Now all I am cries out for more of You,
I want more of You;
More of Your Spirit poured from above,
More of Your power, more of Your love.

1205 Brian Doerksen
Copyright © 1998 Vineyard Songs (UK/Eire)/
Adm. by CopyCare

COME, NOW IS THE TIME to worship,
Come, now is the time to give your heart.
Come, just as you are to worship,
Come, just as you are before your God.
Come.

One day every tongue will confess You are
　God.
One day every knee will bow.
Still, the greatest treasure remains for those
Who gladly choose You now.

1206 Keith Getty & Kristyn Lennox
Copyright © 2002 Thankyou Music

COME, PRAISE THE LORD,
He is life in all its fullness;
Will you lift your voice?
Come, praise the Lord,
He is light that shatters darkness;
We have come to rejoice.
All around the world He is calling
People who would take up His call
And follow Him.

Every breath be praise,
Every heart be raised
To the King of all creation.
Every breath be praise,
Every heart be raised
To the Lord of all.

Come, praise the Lord,
He is love that welcomes sinners;
Will you give your life?
Come praise the Lord,
He is great above all others;
All His ways are right.
All around the world He is calling
People who would take up His call
And follow Him.

1207 Martin E. Leckebusch
Copyright © 2000 Kevin Mayhew Ltd

COME, SEE THE LORD in His breathtaking
  splendour:
Gaze at His majesty – bow and adore!
Enter His presence with wonder and
  worship –
He is the King and enthroned evermore.

He is the Word who was sent by the Father,
Born as a baby, a child of our race:
God here among us, revealed as a servant,
Walking the pathway of truth and of grace.

He is the Lamb who was slain to redeem us –
There at the cross His appearance was
  marred;
Though He emerged from the grave as the
  victor,
Still from the nails and the spear He is
  scarred.

He is the Lord who ascended in triumph –
Ever the sound of His praises shall ring!
Hail Him the First and the Last, the Almighty:
Jesus, our Prophet, our Priest and our King.

Come, see the Lord in His breathtaking
  splendour:
Gaze at His majesty – bow and adore!
Come and acknowledge Him Saviour and
  Sovereign:
Jesus our King is enthroned evermore.

1208 Stuart Townend
Copyright © 1999 Thankyou Music

COME, SEE THIS GLORIOUS LIGHT
As it shines on you,
Bringing grace and peace
To the depths of your soul.
Come, see the wounds of love,
Scars that make you whole,
Blood that paid the price
For the sins of the world.
He is the Light everlasting,
He is the First and the Last.

Blessing and honour and glory and power
Blessing and honour and glory and power
Blessing and honour and glory and power
To You, Lord,
You're the King of the Ages.
Justice and truth are the marks of Your
  reign,
Angels adore You, the Lamb who was
  slain,
They're crying 'holy' again and again,
Lord Jesus,
You're the King of the Ages.

Come, all you thirsty and poor,
Come and feast on Him,
That your souls may live
And be satisfied.
Come from the ends of the earth,
Every tribe and tongue,
Lift your voice and praise
Your eternal Reward.
He's the Desire of the nations,
He is the Faithful and True.

1209 Dave Bilbrough
Copyright © 1999 Thankyou Music

COME TO THE TABLE,
Drink from His cup;
Come to the table,
You can never get enough
Of His love for you,
Of His love for you.
Oh, such precious love.
Oh, such precious love.

Turn your face to Him.
Let the feast begin.
With the angels sing:
Hallelujah, hallelujah,
Hallelujah to the Lord.

We will come to the table,
Drink from Your cup;
Come to the table,
We can never get enough
Of the love You give,
Of the love You give.
Oh, such precious love.
Oh, such precious love.

1210 Martin E. Leckebusch
Copyright © 2000 Kevin Mayhew Ltd

COME, WOUNDED HEALER, Your sufferings
  reveal –
The scars You accepted, our anguish to heal
Your wounds bring such comfort in body an
  soul
To all who bear torment and yearn to be
  whole.

Come, hated Lover, and gather us near,
Your welcome, Your teaching, Your challenge
    to hear:
Where scorn and abuse cause rejection and
    pain,
Your loving acceptance makes hope live
    again!

Come, broken Victor, condemned to a cross –
How great are the treasures we gain from
    Your loss!
Your willing agreement to share in our strife
Transforms our despair into fullness of life.

1211 Matt Redman
Copyright © 1996 Thankyou Music

CREATE IN ME the purest of hearts,
According to Your unfailing love.
Renew a steadfast spirit within
And wash away my sin.
And make me like the snow,
But even whiter still.

I just want to have a pure heart,
I just want to have a pure, pure heart.
I just want to have a pure heart,
I just want to have a pure, pure heart.

I'm clay within the Potter's hand
Where tenderness meets discipline.
I need it all, Lord, come and form
Your holiness in me.
And make me like the snow,
But even whiter still.

1212 Tim Hughes
Copyright © 2001 Thankyou Music

DAY AFTER DAY, I'll search to find You;
Day after day, I'll wait for You.
The deeper I go, the more I love Your name.

So keep my heart pure,
And my ways true,
As I follow You.
Keep me humble,
I'll stay mindful
Of Your mercies, Lord.

I'll cherish Your word,
I'll seek Your presence,
I'll chase after You with all I have.
As one day I know
I'll see You face to face.

1213 Gerard Markland
Copyright © 1978 Kevin Mayhew Ltd

DO NOT BE AFRAID,
For I have redeemed you.
I have called you by your name;
You are Mine.

When you walk through the waters I'll be
    with you;
You will never sink beneath the waves.

When the fire is burning all around you,
You will never be consumed by the flames.

When the fear of loneliness is looming,
Then remember I am at your side.

When you dwell in the exile of the stranger,
Remember you are precious in My eyes.

You are Mine, O My child; I am your Father,
And I love you with a perfect love.

1214 Karen Lafferty
Copyright © 1981 Maranatha! Praise Inc./
Adm. by CopyCare

DON'T BUILD YOUR HOUSE on the sandy
    land,
Don't build it too near the shore.
Well, it may look kind of nice,
But you'll have to build it twice,
Oh, you'll have to build your house once
    more.

You better build your house upon a rock,
Make a good foundation on a solid spot.
Oh, the storms may come and go,
But the peace of God you will know.

(Descant)
Rock of ages, cleft for me,
Let me hide myself in Thee.

1215 Wayne Drain, Noel Richards, Wayne Freeman,
Neil Costello & Bradley Mason
Copyright © 2001 Thankyou Music

DO YOU LOVE TO PRAISE THE LORD? *(echo)*
Do you love to praise the Lord? *(echo)*
Lift your voices high,
Raise your hands to the sky.
(First time)
Make a joyful noise!

(Second time)
Everybody dance!

Praise Him in the dance,
Everybody dance!
Praise Him in the dance,
Everybody dance!

We have come to praise the Lord. *(echo)*
We have come to praise the Lord. *(echo)*
Lift our voices high,
Raise our hands to the sky,
(First time)
Make a joyful noise!

(Second time)
Then we're gonna dance!

We love to praise the Lord;
It's what we're made for.
We love to praise the Lord;
It's in our nature.
We love to praise the Lord,
It's deep within us.
We love to praise the Lord
With everything that's in us *(×3)*
We will dance!

1216 Ian Hannah
Copyright © 2001 Thankyou Music

DRAW ME CLOSER, precious Saviour,
Nearer to Your holy throne;
Let me know Your cleansing power,
As I wait on You alone.
I am nothing without You, Lord,
I am naked, weak and poor;
But in You I find a fullness,
Nothing else can give me more.

When the waters of destruction
Try to sweep me far away,
Jesus, You are still my anchor;
I need never be afraid.
I will cling to You, my Master,
Holding on with surety.
Pressing onward, looking upward,
Until Jesus, You I see.

Help me listen to Your whisper,
Help me live obediently.
Give me courage in the battles,
Strength to face uncertainty.
Help me never to deny You,
But to cross that finish line.
Moving forward, never backward,
To claim the prize as mine.

1217 Kelly Carpenter
Copyright © 1994 Mercy/Vineyard Publishing/
Adm. by CopyCare

DRAW ME CLOSE TO YOU,
Never let me go.
I lay it all down again,
To hear You say that I'm Your friend.
You are my desire,
No one else will do,
'Cause nothing else could take Your place,
To feel the warmth of Your embrace.
Help me find the way,
Bring me back to You.

You're all I want,
You're all I've ever needed.
You're all I want,
Help me know You are near.

1218 Dave Doran
Copyright © 2001 Thankyou Music

DRAW ME NEAR TO YOU;
Can I come so close
That I can hear Your song of love
That heals my broken heart?

> *And I will walk with You,*
> *Another footstep now.*
> *Can we walk on again,*
> *Another footstep now?*
> *I've walked in fields of pain,*
> *I've sheltered in Your love;*
> *In the valley of death's shadow,*
> *I will fear no evil,*
> *For You are here with me.*
> *My comfort be, my comfort be.*

Draw me near to You,
Even closer still,
So I can see Your scars of love
That saved my wounded soul.

1219 Brian Houston & Tom Brock
Copyright © 2002 Thankyou Music

DRAW ME TO YOUR SIDE, Lord,
Let me feel Your breath,
The very breath of life, Lord,
Rest my head upon Your chest.
And hold me in Your arms, Lord,
Wrap me in Your embrace,
Close enough that I can feel
Your breath upon my face.

> *When I cry out in passion,*
> *To love You more than this,*
> *Renew me in Your presence*
> *And refresh me with Your kiss.*

Far too long I've begged You
For Your sweet release,
To be lost in Your presence
And to know the taste of Your lips.
And for a heart like Yours, God,
And for the mind of Christ
To know no shame and no restraint
In my worship sacrifice.

Well, the curse has been broken,
I know the curtain is torn in two,
No child, no man or woman
Need be separated from You.
The lonely and the broken,
Rejected and despised
Run through the gates of grace by faith,
Into the arms of Christ.

1220 David Lyle Morris & Faith Forster
Copyright © 2000 Thankyou Music

DRAWN FROM EVERY TRIBE,
Every tongue and nation,
Gathered before the throne.
Casting down their crowns,
They fall at His feet
And worship the Lord alone.
What a glorious sight,
Dressed in robes of white,
Washed by the blood of the Lamb.

Singing praise and glory,
Wisdom and thanks,
Honour, power and strength
Be to our God, for ever
And ever, amen.

We are those who follow,
Through scenes of fiery trial,
Drawing from wells of grace.
Through the darkest valley
From the depths of pain,
We'll come to that holy place.
We will overcome
By looking to the Lamb
And worshipping face to face.

Never will we hunger,
We'll no longer thirst,
There's shade from the heat of day.
Led to springs of life,
Jesus, our Shepherd,
Will wipe every tear away.
Our God upon the throne
Will shelter all His own
Who worship Him night and day.

All glory and honour and power to Jesus,
All glory and honour and power to Jesus,
Forever and ever and ever and ever,
Forever and ever and ever and ever,
Amen, amen, amen.

1221 Taizé, music: Jacques Berthier (1923–94)
Copyright © Ateliers et Presses de Taizé

EAT THIS BREAD, drink this cup,
Come to Him and never be hungry.
Eat this bread, drink this cup,
Trust in Him and you will not thirst.

(Alternative words)
Jesus Christ, Bread of Life,
Those who come to You will not hunger.
Jesus Christ, risen Lord,
Those who trust in You will not thirst.

1222 William Whiting (1825–78)

ETERNAL FATHER, STRONG TO SAVE,
Whose arm hath bound the restless wave,
Who bidd'st the mighty ocean deep
Its own appointed limits keep:
O hear us when we cry to Thee
For those in peril on the sea.

O Christ, whose voice the waters heard,
And hushed their raging at Thy word,
Who walkedst on the foaming deep,
And calm amid the storm didst sleep:
O hear us when we cry to Thee
For those in peril on the sea.

O Holy Spirit, who didst brood
Upon the waters dark and rude,
And bid their angry tumult cease,
And give, for wild confusion, peace:
O hear us when we cry to Thee
For those in peril on the sea.

O Trinity of love and power,
Our brethren shield in danger's hour;
From rock and tempest, fire and foe,
Protect them wheresoe'er they go:
Thus evermore shall rise to Thee
Glad hymns of praise from land and sea.

1223 Sue Rinaldi & Caroline Bonnett
Copyright © 2001 Thankyou Music

EVERLASTING, ever true,
All creation sings to You.
Ever faithful, living Lord,
Let the sound of praise be heard.

Jesus, You are
All that I am living for
And all that I believe is in You, Jesus,
All that I am living for
And all that I believe is in You.

Never changing, awesome God,
Sing the glory of the Lord.
Ever loving, holy One,
I will praise what You have done.

1224 Lara Martin (Abundant Life Ministries, Bradford, England)
Copyright © 2002 Thankyou Music

EVERY BREATH I BREATHE comes from You,
I'll never take it for granted.
All that I have, all I've ever needed,
You have provided.

You know when I sit, You know when I rise,
You know my thoughts completely.
You hem me in before and behind:
Such love is hard to describe.

You are my God, You are my God.
As long as I have breath I will sing of Your
* greatness.*
You are my source, my all in all,
My first love, the One I love,
You are my God.

Precious to me are Your thoughts, O God;
No wisdom or knowledge is greater.
Praise be to You, Name above all names:
Who reigns forever, ever and ever, *(×3)*
Who reigns forevermore.
You reign forever, ever and ever, *(×3)*
You reign forevermore.

1225 Matt Redman
Copyright © 1998 Thankyou Music

EVERY DAY, I see more of Your beauty.
Every day, I know more of my frailty, Lord.
And I can only hope that I'll be changed,
Even as I look upon Your face.

For the eyes of my heart,
They are on You forever,
They are on You forever.
Yes, the eyes of my heart,
They are on You forever,
They are on You forever.

Every day, I see more of Your greatness.
Every day, I know more of my weakness,
  Lord.
And I can only hope that I'll be changed,
Even as I look upon Your face.

1226 Robin Mark
Copyright © 2001 Thankyou Music

EVERY DAY HE IS WATCHING
From the heavens and the skies.
And He scans the horizon,
Looking for the sign
Of a son or a daughter
With a prodigal heart,
Coming back to the Father of life.

And the Shepherd is searching
For the sheep who's gone astray,
Though there's ninety and nine safe,
At the closing of the day.
His pursuit is relentless,
His obsession divine;
It's the heart of the Father of life.

Oh, His compassion is for everyone.
Yes, for the lost and the afraid.
And if you listen you can hear His voice,
Hear Him calling,
Hear Him calling your name.

Have you seen my belovèd?
He is radiant and most fair.
In the evening He calls me,
I can see His shadow there.
I will rise up to meet Him,
I will run to His side;
To the Son of the Father of life.

Oh, Your compassion is for everyone.
Yes, for the lost and the afraid.
And if I listen I can hear Your voice,
Hear You calling,
Hear You calling my name.

1227 Noel Richards & Wayne Drain
Copyright © 2001 Thankyou Music

EVERY MORNING I will praise You,
Every moment I am Yours.
Every evening I will worship,
Every day I love You more.

I revel in Your mercy,
I marvel at Your grace.
I need a thousand lifetimes
To give You all my praise.

At night, when I am sleeping,
In every waking hour,
I know You will protect me,
My God, my strong high tower.

1228 Dave Wellington
Copyright © 1999 Thankyou Music

FALLING, moving closer,
Deep into You.
Feasting, drinking my fill,
Tasting of You.

Waiting, listening, hoping
Here's where You are.
Craving, calling Your name,
I need You more.

I will hold on,
Hold through the fire,
Cling through the rain,
I long to hear You.
I need You here,
All that You are,
Only Your touch
Will satisfy me.

1229 Love Maria Willis (1824–1908)

FATHER, HEAR THE PRAYER WE OFFER:
Not for ease that prayer shall be,
But for strength, that we may ever
Live our lives courageously.

Not for ever in green pastures
Do we ask our way to be:
But by steep and rugged pathways
Would we strive to climb to Thee.

Not for ever by still waters
Would we idly quiet stay;
But would smite the living fountains
From the rocks along our way.

Be our strength in hours of weakness,
In our wanderings be our Guide;
Through endeavour, failure, danger,
Father, be Thou at our side.

Let our path be bright or dreary,
Storm or sunshine be our share;
May our souls, in hope unweary,
Make Thy work our ceaseless prayer.

1230 Andrew Ulugia & Wayne Huirua
Copyright © 2001 Parachute Music New Zealand/
Adm. by Kingsway Music

FATHER, INTO YOUR COURTS I WILL ENTER,
Maker of heaven and earth,
I tremble in Your holy presence.
Glory, glory in Your sanctuary,
Splendour and majesty, Lord, before You;
All life adores You.

All the earth will declare
That Your love is everywhere.
The fields will exalt, seas resound.
Hear the trees' joyful cry,
Praising You and so will I.
A new song I'll sing,
Lord, I will glorify and bless Your holy
    name.

1231 Darlene Zschech
Copyright © 1995 Darlene Zschech/
Hillsong Publishing/Kingsway Music

FATHER OF LIFE, DRAW ME CLOSER,
Lord, my heart is set on You:
Let me run the race of time
With Your life enfolding mine,
And let the peace of God,
Let it reign.

O Holy Spirit, Lord, my comfort;
Strengthen me, hold my head up high:
And I stand upon Your truth,
Bringing glory unto You,
And let the peace of God,
Let it reign.

O Lord, I hunger for more of You;
Rise up within me, let me know Your truth.
O Holy Spirit, saturate my soul,
And let the life of God fill me now,
Let Your healing power
Breathe life and make me whole,
And the peace of God,
Let it reign.

1232 Geoff Twigg
Copyright © Geoff Twigg/Jubilate Hymns Ltd

FATHER, WE HAVE SINNED AGAINST YOU,
Failed to do what's right;
We have walked alone in darkness,
Hiding from the light.
Father, we have run away
From what we know is true;
Now we turn around and we are
Coming home to You.

We have sinned, (we have sinned)
We have broken Your law,
We're returning once more home to You;
We have sinned, (we have sinned)
We are seeking Your face,
We return by Your grace home to You.

1233 Keith Getty & Kristyn Lennox
Copyright © 2002 Thankyou Music

FIND REST, ALL THE EARTH, in God alone.
We find our only hope from heaven's throne.
Our Rock, our Salvation,
No, we shall not be shaken.
Find rest all the earth in God alone.

His peace holds you firm in the storm.
His love brings new life forevermore.
Our Rock, our Salvation,
No, we shall not be shaken.
His peace holds you firm in the storm.

Tell of the One who lifted your soul,
Share all His goodness.
Children of light declaring the truth,
That all may know.

1234 Fred Pratt Green (1903–2000)
Copyright © 1970 Stainer & Bell Ltd

FOR THE FRUITS OF HIS CREATION,
Thanks be to God!
For His gifts to every nation,
Thanks be to God!
For the ploughing, sowing, reaping,
Silent growth while we are sleeping;
Future needs in earth's safe keeping,
Thanks be to God!

In the just reward of labour,
God's will is done;
In the help we give our neighbour,
God's will is done;
In our worldwide task of caring
For the hungry and despairing,
In the harvests we are sharing,
God's will is done.

For the harvests of His Spirit,
Thanks be to God!
For the good we all inherit,
Thanks be to God!
For the wonders that astound us,
For the truths that still confound us;
Most of all, that love has found us,
Thanks be to God!

1235 Fred Kaan
Copyright © 1968 Stainer & Bell Ltd

FOR THE HEALING OF THE NATIONS,
Lord, we pray with one accord;
For a just and equal sharing
Of the things that earth affords.
To a life of love in action
Help us rise and pledge our word.

Lead us forward into freedom;
From despair Your world release,
That, redeemed from war and hatred,
All may come and go in peace.
Show us how through care and goodness
Fear will die and hope increase.

All that kills abundant living,
Let it from the earth be banned;
Pride of status, race or schooling,
Dogmas that obscure Your plan.
In our common quest for justice
May we hallow life's brief span.

You, Creator-God, have written
Your great name on humankind;
For our growing in Your likeness
Bring the life of Christ to mind;
That by our response and service
Earth its destiny may find.

1236 Lynn DeShazo & Gary Sadler
Copyright © 1997 Integrity's Hosanna! Music/
Sovereign Music UK

FOR THE LORD IS GOOD,
And His love endures forever;
He's a faithful God
To all generations.
For the Lord is good,
And His mercies will not fail us;
They are new each day,
O, lift your voice and say,
'The Lord is good!'

Great is Your faithfulness, O Lord. *(Leader)*
Great is Your faithfulness, O Lord. *(Echo)*
Your loving kindness fills our *(Leader)*
Hearts to overflowing. *(All)*
Songs of rejoicing and sweet praise, *(Leade*
Songs of praise! *(Echo)*
They fill our hearts, *(Leader)*
They fill our hearts, *(Echo)*
They fill our days. *(All)*

1237 Charles Wesley (1707–88)

FORTH IN THY NAME, O LORD, I GO,
My daily labour to pursue,
Thee, only Thee, resolved to know
In all I think, or speak, or do.

The task Thy wisdom hath assigned
O let me cheerfully fulfil;
In all my works Thy presence find,
And prove Thy acceptable will.

Thee may I set at my right hand,
Whose eyes my inmost substance see;
And labour on at Thy command,
And offer all my works to Thee.

Give me to bear Thy easy yoke,
And every moment watch and pray,
And still to things eternal look,
And hasten to Thy glorious day.

For Thee delightfully employ
Whate'er Thy bounteous grace hath given,
And run my course with even joy,
And closely walk with Thee to heaven.

1238

FROM THE RISING OF THE SUN,
Even to its going down,
Shall Your name be great.
Through all the earth,
Among the nations, we give You praise;
Your name is high above
All other gods.

Jesus, Lover of my soul,
You alone are King, worthy of my praise.
My worship I'll give to only one;
O Lord, my heart I'll bring
When to You I come.

Holiness, Majesty and King,
Let Your will be done
When we worship bring.
Eternal, Your love will remain;
Before Your throne we bow,
With our voices sing.

1239

**FROM THE SQUALOR OF A BORROWED
STABLE,**
By the Spirit and a virgin's faith;
To the anguish and the shame of scandal
Came the Saviour of the human race!
But the skies were filled with the praise of
heaven,
Shepherds listen as the angels tell
Of the Gift of God come down to man
At the dawning of Immanuel.

King of heaven now the Friend of sinners,
Humble servant in the Father's hands,
Filled with power and the Holy Spirit,
Filled with mercy for the broken man.
Yes, He walked my road and He felt my pain,
Joys and sorrows that I know so well;
Yet His righteous steps give me hope again –
Will follow my Immanuel!

Through the kisses of a friend's betrayal,
He was lifted on a cruel cross;
He was punished for a world's
transgressions,
He was suffering to save the lost.
He fights for breath, He fights for me,
Loosing sinners from the claims of hell;
And with a shout our souls are free –
Death defeated by Immanuel!

Now He's standing in the place of honour,
Crowned with glory on the highest throne,
Interceding for His own belovèd
Till His Father calls to bring them home!
Then the skies will part as the trumpet
sounds
Hope of heaven or the fear of hell;
But the Bride will run to her Lover's arms,
Giving glory to Immanuel!

1240

GIVER OF GRACE,
How priceless Your love for me,
Purer than silver, more costly than gold.
Giver of life, all that I'll ever need,
Strength for my body and food for my soul.

Oh, You are good, so good to me.
Yes, You are good, so good to me.
Oh, You are good, so good to me.
Yes, You are good, so good to me

Giver of hope, Rock of salvation,
Tower of refuge, yet there in my pain.
Now I'm secure, loved for eternity,
Showered with blessings
And lavished with grace.

I've never known a love
So perfect in its faithfulness;
It lifts me up to the highest place.
A glimpse of heaven
And a taste of my inheritance,
I know that one day I'll be with You.

1241

GIVE THANKS TO THE LORD,
Our God and King:
His love endures forever.
For He is good, He is above all things.
His love endures forever.
Sing praise, sing praise.

With a mighty hand
And an outstretched arm
His love endures forever.
For the life that's been reborn.
His love endures forever.
Sing praise, sing praise.
Sing praise, sing praise.

Forever God is faithful,
Forever God is strong.
Forever God is with us,
Forever.
(Repeat)
Forever.

From the rising to the setting sun,
His love endures forever.
By the grace of God, we will carry on.
His love endures forever.
Sing praise, sing praise.
Sing praise, sing praise.

1242 Geraldine Latty
Copyright © 2000 Thankyou Music

GIVING IT ALL TO YOU,
Giving it all to You,
No more hidden agenda,
Giving it all to You.
Laying my burdens down,
Bowing in full surrender,
Kneeling before Your cross,
Giving it all to You.

1243 Kate & Miles Simmonds
Copyright © 2002 Thankyou Music

GOD GAVE US HIS SON,
The sinless One to be sin for us,
That we might be the righteousness of God.
Your kingdom has come,
We're being changed into Your likeness;
Children of light, it's our time to arise.

I am not ashamed,
I know whom I've believed,
For God Himself has come to me,
Now Jesus is my destiny.
I know I am changed,
And all You've given me,
This hope, this love, this life,
I can't deny Your power within me.
So here I am, send me.

Now we are in You,
And You have given us Your message
To tell the world: be reconciled to God.
Your favour is here
In this day of salvation.
Now is the time, let Your glory arise!

Purify us, Lord,
So we're spotless and pure
As we hold out Your word
To this generation.
How can they hear,
And how can they believe,
How can they call on Your name
Unless we tell them?
(Repeat)

1244 Don Moen & Paul Overstreet
Copyright © 1995 Integrity's Hosanna! Music/
Sovereign Music UK/Scarlet Moon Music/
Adm. by Copyright Management Services

GOD IS GOOD ALL THE TIME!
He put a song of praise in this heart of
mine.
God is good all the time!
Through the darkest night
His light will shine:
God is good, God is good all the time.

If you're walking through the valley
And there are shadows all around,
Do not fear, He will guide you,
He will keep you safe and sound;
'Cause He has promised to never leave you
Nor forsake you, and His word is true.

We were sinners, so unworthy,
Still for us He chose to die:
Filled us with His Holy Spirit,
Now we can stand and testify
That His love is everlasting
And His mercies, they will never end.

Though I may not understand
All the plans You have for me,
My life is in Your hands,
And through the eyes of faith
I can clearly see:

1245 David Lyle Morris & Nick Wynne-Jones
Copyright © 2001 Thankyou Music

GOD IS OUR FATHER in heaven above,
And He cares for His children with infinite
love.
Our worries are needless; look up in the sky
Where carefree and singing the birds freely
fly.
Their Maker who knows them,
Supplies all their food;
How much more is our Father
Concerned for our good?

For our Father in heaven
Knows all of our needs;
He will care for us always.
We surrender our all,
And make the kingdom of heaven our
*   goal.*

Look at the lilies and see how they grow:
They are clothed by God's goodness in
    beautiful show.
Our Father in heaven who cares for each
    flower,
Provides for us always, so great is His power.
The kingdom of heaven
And His righteousness
We will seek with a passion
So all may be blessed.

1246 Louise Fellingham
Copyright © 2002 Thankyou Music

GOD OF MERCY, hear our cry,
Turn Your hand today.
Bring relief from their pain,
Be their comfort.
And every day they're given breath,
Give them strength to live.
And as their weary bodies fail,
Fighting is over, flesh gives way,
Be their light to guide them home.

God of mercy, hear our cry,
Heal their souls today.
Give them peace from their fears,
Be their hope, Lord.
And every day they're given breath,
Give them strength to live.
And as their weary bodies fail,
Fighting is over, flesh gives way,
Be their star to guide them home.

Sometimes I don't know what to ask for,
Sometimes I don't know what to say,
But I know that You are watching over them.
Sometimes I don't know what to pray for,
Sometimes I don't know how to give,
But I know that You are watching over them,
And their life is not in vain.

1247 Matt Redman
Copyright © 1998 Thankyou Music

GOD OF RESTORATION,
My hope is in the life You bring to me.
Healer of my wounds,
thank You, oh I thank You.
God of my salvation,
With saving love You came to rescue me.
Healer of my soul,
thank You, oh I thank You,
Today and every day.

I am Yours, I am Yours,
Every breath that I breathe,
Every moment that's lived.
I am Yours, I am Yours,
You're the reason to breathe,
You're the reason to live.
And now everyone that You have saved
Will come to be Your praise,
I am Yours.

Singing of a love now,
You taught this broken heart to sing again.
Every day I'll come
To thank You, oh, to thank You.
Singing of a life now,
You taught this wounded soul to live again.
Every day I'll live
To thank You, oh, to thank You,
Today and every day.

And if my food is to do Your will,
Then I'm hungry, still hungry;
There's so much more that I need to give
To thank You, to thank You.
Yes, if my food is to do Your will,
Then I'm hungry, still hungry;
There's so much more that I need to give
Today and every day.

1248 Sue Rinaldi, Caroline Bonnett & Steve Bassett
Copyright © 2001 Thankyou Music

GOD OF THE MOUNTAINS,
God of the sea;
God of the heavens
Of eternity.
God of the future,
God of the past;
God of the present,
God of all history.

Creation praise will thunder to You,
Thunder to You, thunder to You.
Creation praise will thunder to You.
I'm lost in the wonder,
Lost in the wonder of You.

Wisdom of ages,
Light in the dark;
Home for the outcast,
Peace for the heart.
Friend of the lonely,
Strength for oppressed;
Voice of the voiceless,
God of all liberty.

1249 Brian Houston
Copyright © 2002 Thankyou Music

GOD, YOU ARE GOOD, God, You are kind.
God, You are sun, God, You are shine.
God, You are truth, God, You are pure.
You've melted my heart,
And now I am Yours.

I'm happy to be a friend of God.
I'm happy that God's a friend to me.

You're bursting with love
For the ones that You made.
You're happy to bless
Every one of their days.
You humble the proud
But You raise up the low.
You cry for the lost
But You eat with the poor.

And You love me so much
That You weep for my pain,
And You guide with Your touch.
For it is not Your heart to see me fall,
Or let my sin remain.

1250 Gareth Robinson
Copyright © 2001 Thankyou Music

GOOD AND GRACIOUS,
Attributes of a loving Father,
You're high and mighty,
But humble all the same.
You have made the heavens and the earth,
And You made us in Your image, Lord.

Holy, holy, holy is the Lord Almighty,
And we rejoice in You alone,
For You are worthy.
And You have given life to me,
And I love to worship at Your feet,
And I love to love You just for who You are.

Death and hell are
Now no longer things I fear because
You have saved me
And I'm grateful to the core.
I'm Your child because of Jesus' blood,
And Your Spirit leads me,
Guides me, fills me.

I'm so grateful for the things
You have given me:
Your love, Your grace, Your joy,
Your peace and more.
Holy, holy.
Holy, holy.

1251 Dave Bilbrough
Copyright © 2000 Thankyou Music

GRACE AND MERCY wash over me,
Cleanse my soul with Your healing stream.
Here I stand with this prayer within my heart.
Take me deeper in the river that flows with
    Your love.

Thank You, thank You,
Oh what riches are mine in Christ Jesus.
Thank You, thank You,
Your forgiveness is so undeserved.

1252 Ian Hannah
Copyright © 2001 Thankyou Music

GREAT AND MARVELLOUS are Your deeds,
    Lord;
Just and true are all of Your ways.
Who would dare to never fear You,
Or bring glory to Your name.
For nothing compares to You.

You are worthy to receive all
Of the glory, honour and power.
By You all things were created
And by You all things are sustained.
For nothing compares to You.
No, nothing compares to You.

Every nation rise and sing
Praises to our glorious King.
Every tongue in one accord
Cry out and confess:
'Jesus is Lord!'

'Hallelujah' cry Your servants,
'We will worship' both great and small.
King of all kings, Lord of all lords,
You will reign for evermore.
For nothing compares to You.
No, nothing compares to You.

1253 Geraldine Latty & Carey Luce
Copyright © 2002 Thankyou Music

GREAT AND MARVELLOUS are Your deeds,
O God, sovereign over all,
Just and righteous in every way.
Great King for all time eternal.
Who shall not fear You, Lord?
Who shall not honour Your name?
Who shall not fear You, Lord?
There is none the same.

All the nations, every race,
Coming now to seek Your face.
Singing to the Holy One,
Jesus Christ, God's only Son.
All the people in this place,
Thanking You for saving grace,
Burdens rolled to Calvary,
Once in chains but now set free.

Great and marvellous are Your deeds,
O Lord, how we long to see Your
Plan in our time revealed:
Hearts longing to worship Jesus.
And we will fear You, Lord;
And we will honour Your name.
Yes, we will fear You, Lord:
There is none the same.

1254

GREAT IS HE who's the King of kings
And the Lord of lords,
He is wonderful!

Alleluia, alleluia,
Alleluia, He is wonderful!

Alleluia, salvation and glory,
Honour and power, He is wonderful!

1255

HALLELUJAH, HOSANNA,
Hallelujah, hosanna,
Hallelujah, hosanna,
Hallelujah, hosanna!
(Repeat)

God has exalted Jesus to the highest place,
And given Him the name that is above every
name,
That at the name of Jesus every knee shall
bow
And every tongue confess that He is Lord.

Hallalango Jesu, hallalango Jesu,
Hallalango Jesu, hallala O hallala.
Hallalango Jesu, hallalango Jesu,
Hallalango Jesu, Nkosi!

1256

HAVE I NOT BEEN FAITHFUL to You, Lord?
Have I not offered up my prayers
And tried to follow Your word?
Lord, will You search me,
Show me where I'm wrong?

I've been waiting for the blessing
For far too long,
I've been waiting for the blessing
For far too long.

Now Lord, forgive me,
For speaking this right out.
But I see the wicked prosper
While the godly go without.
No, I can't read human hearts,
But do You know where I'm coming from?

Do not be angry with me, O my God,
Please don't hide Your face away.
I'm like a child, and I'm down on my knees
And I'm begging for You
Just to bless me today.

Lord, up ahead You know
I see a lonely road.
Got this burden on my back,
It's such a heavy load.
These days I've questions,
But there's no answers in my songs.

1257

HAVE WE FORGOTTEN the price that's been
paid?
Have we remembered the wage of our ways?
Can we dismiss what He's done on the cross
As foolishness?
Oh, thank You, oh, thank You.

O Saviour and Friend,
Redeemer of many,
You poured out Your blood to me,
And gave up Your life for me.
(Oh, thank You.)

It was my life He paid with His pain,
Suffered at the hands of those He had made.
Can we consider what He once went through
To be with us?
Oh, thank You, oh, thank You.

Oh, how can I repay such a love?
Oh, how can I repay such a love?
How can I repay such a love?
Oh, thank You.

1258

HEAR ALL CREATION lift its voice,
The mountains sing and the rivers rejoice
For the name of Jesus,
For His name.
And we His people saved by grace,
We bow our hearts and we bring our praise
To the sweet Redeemer,
For His name.

So with everything we are,
And everything we have
We pour out our offerings.
And if ever we should fail,
The rocks will rise up
And crown Him the King of kings.

He mends our hearts, He keeps our ways:
He lights our nights and He leads our days,
All for His glory, for His name.
There's nothing greater than to be His,
To bring Him glory and to fully live
For the name of Jesus,
For His name.

1259

HEAR MY CONFESSION in Your compassion;
Could You lead me in the way that I should
go?
If I lose my life for You, I know I'll find it;
Could Your will become incarnate in my soul?

For I would rather learn to open doors in Your
house,
Than spend the rest of my days wasted
somewhere else.
For I could never be free or feel Your peace
Till I surrender to Your love.

Take my whole heart;
I won't hold back the least part.
I wanna fall face forward
Into the arms of grace.
Oh, may my passion become so
undivided
That I won't be satisfied with nothing less,
Nothing less than You.

Could You give me a hunger for Your
kingdom,
That my own desires would all take second
place?

1260

HEAR MY MOUTH SPEAK, see my mind
think,
Know my spirit tries to pray.
Lord, we're longing to see You moving,
Help us as we pray today.
Words don't seem enough to tell You our
desire,
To see Your kingdom come and Your light
shine.

Light of the world, would You shine on
me?
Light of the world, would You shine on
me?

Now I trust You, and I ask You,
Let Your will be done in me.
May Your light shine in all the earth and
Let it draw us all to You.
Now Your glory shines throughout Your holy
church,
'Cause You're our only hope, Saviour of the
world.

Shine on me so I reflect Your glory,
Live in me so people see Your beauty,
Pour on me, so out of me flow streams of
living water.
(Repeat)

1261

HEAR MY PRAYER, O LORD,
From the ends of the earth I cry.
Your peace will lead me to
The Rock that is higher than I.
(Repeat)

For You have been my strength in times of
trouble,
A tower above my enemies.
And Lord, I will abide with you forever
In the shelter of Your wings.
(Repeat)

1262

HEAR OUR CRY for the nations,
O Lord of the heavens.
Hear our prayer for this fallen world.
Come by Your Spirit,
Pour out Your mercy
On this earth.

Hear our cry for this nation,
O Lord of the heavens.
Hear our prayer as we gather here.
Come by Your Spirit,
Pour out Your mercy,
Heal this land.

1263 Don Moen
Copyright © 2000 Integrity's Hosanna! Music/
Sovereign Music UK

HEAR OUR PRAYER, we are Your children,
And we've gathered here today.
We've gathered here to pray.
Hear our cry, Lord, we need Your mercy
And we need Your grace today,
Hear us as we pray.

Our Father, who art in heaven,
Hallowed be Thy name.
Our Father, hear us from heaven,
Forgive our sins, we pray.

Hear our song as it rises to heaven,
May Your glory fill the earth
As the waters cover the sea.
See our hearts and remove anything
That is standing in the way
Of coming to You today.

And though we are few, we're surrounded by
  many
Who have crossed that river before,
And this is the song we'll be singing forever:
Holy is the Lord, holy is the Lord,
Holy is the Lord, holy is the Lord.

1264 Gareth Robinson & Joannah Oyeniran
Copyright © 2002 Thankyou Music

HEAR OUR PRAYERS and hear our longing,
Hear our cry, O Lord.
Save the people, broken, hurting,
Lost without Your love.

How long will it be, O Lord,
How long will it be?
How long will it be, O Lord,
How long will it be?

1265 Ken Riley
Copyright © 2001 Thankyou Music

HEAVEN OPENED and You came to save me.
You were broken and became sin for me.
No death, no hate, no shame,
No slave again to fear;
New life, new hope, new love,
Your kingdom's coming near.

And I give You praise
And I lift my hands to You,
All of my days
I will bring my love to You.
I will give my life as an offering,
As a sacrifice to the coming King of grace,
Jesus.

You have risen from the grave forever.
Through eternity I'll praise my Saviour.
No death, no hate, no shame,
No slave again to fear;
New life, new hope, new love,
Your kingdom's coming near.

I love and adore You,
And live for Your praise.
In truth and in spirit
I long for You, my King.

1266 Dave Bilbrough
Copyright © 2002 Thankyou Music

HE DIED FOR MY SAKE,
Though I was a sinner;
Redeemed me by His grace,
To know His love forever.

With every breath that I take,
And every beat of my heart
I live to give Him worship,
And to make His glory known.
(Repeat)

1267 Ken Riley
Copyright © 1999 Thankyou Music

HE IS HOLY, HOLY, HOLY,
My Lord is holy, holy, holy, Jesus.
Give glory, glory, glory to the Son,
Glory, glory, glory to Jesus!

We're gonna give Him praise,
And His name we'll raise
As we celebrate with Jesus.
Let our voices sing to the King of kings,
Who was and is to come.

He's the Prince of Peace
And He will release
All the chains that keep you down.
He's the Son of Man,
He's the Great I Am,
He's the mighty Lamb of heaven!

He's the God of grace,
And if we seek His face
He'll demonstrate His power.
On the final day unto the bride He'll say:
'At My side you'll stay forever and ever.'

1268 David Lyle Morris & Nick Wynne-Jones

HE ONCE WAS DEAD, BUT NOW HE LIVES:
The First, the Last, the Living One.
He holds the keys of death and hell:
The First, the Last, the Living One.

More love, our hearts on fire.
More power, so faith stands strong.
More life, both real and pure.
More faith that holds the truth.
More, Lord, of You within Your church.
You, Lord, are King most glorious.

We hear Your voice, we come to You:
The First, the Last, the Living One.
We will obey and follow You:
The First, the Last, the Living One.

The First, the Last, the Living One.
Lord, by Your word we overcome.
We live our lives to You alone:
The First, the Last, the Living One.

You, Lord, the One who knows us.
You, Lord, the love that calls us.
You, Lord, have power to keep us.
You, Lord, speak words of promise.
You, Lord, the life victorious.
You, Lord, are King most glorious.

You once were dead, but now You live:
The First, the Last, the Living One.
You hold the keys of death and hell:
The First, the Last, the Living One.

1269 Matt Redman

HERE AM I, A SINNER FREE,
Pardoned by Your majesty,
Your love has led me into liberty.
Holy King, upon the throne,
You've made this heart Your very own.
I feel like the leper who's been healed.

Lost and dirty, yet You found me.
Stained by sin, but You have cleansed me.
Can it be I'm precious in Your sight?
What is man, and who am I?
A child of God, my Father's pride,
What a joy to be the Lord's delight.

I have known a love so sweet,
A saving love that brings relief,
A healing love that makes the blind eye see.
King of Love and Prince of Peace,
Your Shepherd's love is tending me –
A love that satisfies my deepest needs.

1270 Andrew Ulugia

HERE I AM, O GOD,
I bring this sacrifice,
My open heart, I offer up my life.
I look to You, Lord,
Your love that never ends
Restores me again.

So I lift my eyes to You, Lord,
In Your strength I will break through, Lord.
Touch me now, let Your love fall down on me.
I know Your love dispels all my fears.
Through the storm I will hold on, Lord,
And by faith I will walk on, Lord,
Then I'll see beyond my Calvary one day,
And I will be complete in You.

1271 Reuben Morgan

HERE I AM WAITING,
Abide in me I pray.
Here I am longing for You.
Hide me in Your love,
Bring me to my knees.
May I know Jesus more and more.

Come, live in me all my life,
Take over.
Come, breathe in me and I will rise
On eagles' wings.
(Repeat)

1272 Ken Riley

HERE IN YOUR ARMS,
I am lost in Your love.
Holding me close,
Never let me fall.

I will worship You,
I will worship You,
Oh I, I will worship You, Lord.

Here, face to face,
I am lost in praise.
Love's hunger grows,
Burning stronger still.

1273 Words: Revelation 3:20 / Paraphrase John L. Bell
Copyright © 1995 WGRG, Iona Community

(First part)
HERE I STAND at the door and knock, and knock.
I will come and dine with those who ask me in.

(Second part)
Here I stand at the door and knock, and knock.
I will dine with those who ask me in.

1274 James Gregory
Copyright © 2000 Thankyou Music

HERE I STAND, longing to meet with God;
I have come, bringing a grateful heart.
And I will sing of this amazing love again.
Here I am, falling before Your throne,
For my King laying down any crown,
And I'll sing of this amazing love again.

Here I am before Your throne of grace;
I can come, for You have made a way,
And I'll sing of this amazing love again.
Here I am, so overwhelmed by You;
I come near, for I belong to You,
And I'll sing of this amazing love again.

I am in love with God,
I am in love with God,
I hear You call my name,
I give my heart again.
I am in love with God,
I am in love with God,
I hear You call my name,
I'm on my knees again.

You have won my heart and I can say
That I could find no other way.
Now I am Yours, and here I'll stay
To offer up this praise.

I'm in love with You,
I'm in love with You.

1275 Tim Sherrington
Copyright © 2000 Thankyou Music

HERE I WAIT BENEATH THE CROSS,
Resting in the presence of Your love.
Here I wait to know Your heart,
As I worship You in spirit and in truth.

For You are my God,
You are my King,
You reveal deep within to my very soul.
For You alone are

Jesus, there's no other name,
Jesus, eternally the same,
Jesus, the King of kings.
Jesus, Redeemer, Saviour, Friend,
Jesus, faithful till the end,
Jesus, the King of kings.

Here I come to give my all,
My hands reach up in holy praise to You.
Here I cast all chains aside
To worship You in spirit and in truth.

1276 Kevin Prosch
Copyright © 1996 Kevin Prosch/
Adm. by Kingsway Music

HEY LORD, (Hey Lord),
O LORD, (O Lord),
Hey Lord, (Hey Lord),
You know what we need.
(Repeat)

Na na na na na na na,
Na na na na na na na,
Na na na na na na na na.

Jesus, (Jesus),
You're the One (You're the One),
You set my heart (You set my heart)
On fire (on fire).
(Repeat)

1277 Robin Mark
Copyright © 2000 Thankyou Music

HOLY, HOLY, holy, holy
Is the Lord God Almighty.
Holy, holy, holy, holy
Is the song around the throne.
Where the angels and the elders gather
There in sweet assembly,
Singing holy, singing holy
Is the Lord our God.

Worthy, worthy, worthy, worthy
Is the Lamb who was slain for me.
Worthy, worthy, worthy, worthy
Is the song within my heart.
I could choose to spend eternity
With this my sole refrain:
Singing worthy, singing worthy
Is the Lord our God.

The Way, the Truth, the Life, the Light,
The King, the Great I Am.
My life, my all, my every breath,
The Rock on which I stand.

Oh Jesus, oh Jesus,
How You suffered and died for us.
Oh Jesus, oh Jesus,
But that tomb is empty now.
And I long to gaze upon Your throne
And all Your risen glory:
Singing Jesus, singing Jesus
Is the Lord of all.

1278
Dave Bilbrough
Copyright © 1999 Thankyou Music

HOLY, HOLY is the Lord our God;
Who was and is and is to come,
And evermore shall be.

With a grateful heart I will give my praise
To the Lamb upon the throne;
King of ages, Lord of life,
Exalted over all.

1279
Reuben Morgan
Copyright © 2002 Reuben Morgan/
Hillsong Publishing/Kingsway Music

HOLY, HOLY ARE YOU, LORD,
The whole earth is filled with Your glory.
Let the nations rise to give
Honour and praise to Your name.
Let Your face shine on us
And the world will know You live.

All the heavens shout Your praise,
Beautiful is our God,
The universe will sing
Hallelujah to You, our King.

1280
Brenton Brown
Copyright © 2001 Vineyard Songs (UK/Eire)/
Adm. by CopyCare

HOLY, HOLY, GOD ALMIGHTY,
Who was and is to come.
God of glory, You're so worthy,
All the saints bow down.

Holy is Your name in all the earth.
Righteous are Your ways, so merciful.
Everything You've done is just and true.
Holy, holy God are You.
Holy, holy God are You.

All blessing, all honour belongs to You.
All power, all wisdom is Yours.

1281
Author unknown (Argentina)
Spanish and English Copyright Control

HOLY, HOLY, HOLY,
My heart, my heart adores You!
My heart is glad to say the words:
You are holy, Lord.

Santo, santo, santo,
Mí corazón te adora!
Mí corazón te sabe decir:
Santo eres Señor.

1282
Keith Getty, Emma Vardy & Noel Robinson
Copyright © 2001 Thankyou Music

HOLY, HOLY, HOLY LORD,
God of power and might.
Earth and heaven worship You,
Your majesty so bright.
Yet we, Your fallen children know
Your love beyond compare.
We lift our hands, surrender
To grace so undeserved.

Before You, Lord, forgiven,
We bow before Your throne.
At Your cross, we find in You
Our righteousness restored.
Before You, Lord, forgiven,
We stand in Your great love,
And live our lives in honour
To Your forgiving blood.

Living in Your presence, Lord,
Sin and guilt atoned;
Citizens of heaven,
Heirs unto Your throne.
To be with You in glory,
To see You face to face,
At last home with the Father,
Our holy dwelling place.

1283
Andrew Ulugia
Copyright © 1998 Parachute Music New Zealand,
Adm. by Kingsway Music

HOLY ONE, righteous King,
Merciful You are:
Merciful I'll be.
Broken One, bruised for me,
In Your death, O Lord,
You have set me free.

Because Your Father loved me so,
You came to me, Lord Jesus,
So that I would know
Love unconditional and life eternal,
O my Lord, my God, my all.

Risen One, Majesty,
Restoration, come
Breathe new life in me.
(Repeat)

1284 Peter Brooks, Stuart Townend & Kate Simmonds
Copyright © 2002 Thankyou Music

HOLY SPIRIT, HOW I LOVE YOU;
Holy Spirit, flood my soul.
Holy Spirit, take me over;
Holy Spirit, lead me on.

You're the Strength that helps me in my
weakness,
You're the Friend who comes to walk beside;
You're the peace that passes understanding,
As You reign in my life.

1285 Russell Fragar
Copyright © 1997 Russell Fragar/
Hillsong Publishing/Kingsway Music

HOLY SPIRIT, RAIN DOWN, rain down.
O Comforter and Friend,
How we need Your touch again.
Holy Spirit, rain down, rain down.
Let Your power fall,
Let Your voice be heard,
Come and change our hearts,
As we stand on Your word.
Holy Spirit, rain down.

No eye has seen, no ear has heard,
No mind can know what God has in store.
So open up heaven, open it wide
Over Your church, and over our lives.
(Repeat)

1286 Joel Houston
Copyright © 2000 Joel Houston/
Hillsong Publishing/Kingsway Music

HOPE HAS FOUND ITS HOME WITHIN ME,
Now that I've been found in You.
Let all I am be all You want me to be,
'Cause all I want is more of You,
All I want is more of You.

Let Your presence fall upon us,
I want to see You face to face;
Let me live forever lost in Your love,
'Cause all I want is more of You,
All I want is more of You.

I'm living for this cause,
I lay down my life
Into Your hands.
I'm living for the truth,
The hope of the world,
In You I'll stand.
All I want is You.

All I want is,
All I want is You, Jesus.

1287 Elwood H. Stokes (1815–95)

HOVER O'ER ME, Holy Spirit,
Bathe my trembling heart and brow;
Fill me with Thy hallowed presence,
Come, O come and fill me now.

Fill me now, fill me now,
Jesus, come and fill me now.
Fill me with Thy hallowed presence,
Jesus, come and fill me now.

Thou can fill me, gracious Spirit,
Though I cannot tell Thee how;
But I need Thee, greatly need Thee,
Come, O come and fill me now.

I am weakness, full of weakness,
At Thy sacred feet I bow;
Blest, divine, eternal Spirit,
Come with power, and fill me now.

1288 Lara Martin (Abundant Life Ministries,
Bradford, England)
Copyright © 2002 Thankyou Music

HOW CAN I NOT PRAISE YOU,
When I consider all You've done?
God of creation, all sufficient One.
How can I not worship
When I consider who You are?
You are my Master,
The One who has my heart.

Hallelujah, praise the Lord, O my soul.
Hallelujah, it is You I adore.
Hallelujah, hallelujah, hallelujah.
Hallelujah, I am saved! I am saved!
Hallelujah, free to praise Your name.
Hallelujah, hallelujah, hallelujah.

How can I not love You,
When Your love reached deep down to me?
Love so amazing, what a mystery.
How can I not give my all,
When You gave heaven's best to me?
Jesus, my treasure for all eternity.

1289 Geraldine Latty
Copyright © 2000 Thankyou Music

HOW CAN I REPAY YOU, Lord,
For all You've done for me?
Nothing I can say or do
Will ever be enough.

I will live for You,
Walking in Your way,
Lifting high Your name,
Holding close the cross.
Not in words alone,
But in what I do,
I will live my life for You.

Dear Lord, Your heart is drawing me,
A calling from Your throne.
And in my brokenness I come
And whisper to You, Lord.

It's not by works, but by Your grace,
I'll never earn Your love.
You loved me first, You'll love me last,
Your cross, my only hope.

1290 Lara Martin (Abundant Life Ministries,
Bradford, England)
Copyright © 2002 Thankyou Music

HOW GOOD YOU HAVE BEEN TO ME,
Forever faithful.
How true are Your promises,
Never shaken.
You are the Light of my life,
You are the reason I live.

I live for You,
I place no one above You.
I'll walk with You always, always.
To talk with You,
And feel Your breath on my face,
How amazing,
How amazing You are!

How rich is Your word, O Lord,
At work within me.
How soft is Your voice I hear,
That gently calls me.
Each day I wake to Your love;
I know that I am blessed of God!

1291 Lynn DeShazo
Copyright © 1999 Integrity's Hosanna! Music/
Sovereign Music UK

HOW GREAT ARE YOU, LORD,
How great is Your mercy,
How great are the things
That You have done for me.
How great are You, Lord,
Your loving kindness
Is filling my heart as I sing,
How great are You, Lord.

How great is Your love,
It reaches to the heavens;
How great is the heart
That sought and rescued me.

1292 Neil Bennetts
Copyright © 2002 Thankyou Music

HOW SHALL I FIND my place of rest,
True wisdom and the hand of God?
Not by my own understanding,
But by Your Spirit in me.

How shall I know the kind of love
That cannot fade, that cannot fail?
Not from this world's empty treasure,
But by the promise of God.

For You are the strength in my heart,
So faithful when other loves fail me.
Forever the strength in my heart:
Jesus, Jesus.

Your river flows, it covers me,
Its blessing fills my life always,
And sets my eyes on Your beauty
And fills my heart with a song.

1293 Kathryn Scott
Copyright © 1999 Vineyard Songs (UK/Eire)/
Adm. by CopyCare

HUNGRY, I COME TO YOU,
For I know You satisfy.
I am empty, but I know
Your love does not run dry.
So I wait for You,
So I wait for You.

I'm falling on my knees,
Offering all of me.
Jesus, You're all this heart is living for.

Broken, I run to You,
For Your arms are open wide;
I am weary, but I know
Your touch restores my life.
So I wait for You,
So I wait for You.

1294 Lara Martin (Abundant Life Ministries, Bradford, England)
Copyright © 2000 Lara Martin/Abundant Life Ministries/Adm. by Kingsway Music

I AM AMAZED
By the power of Your grace,
I am amazed
That You took my sin and shame;
Restoring hope, restoring dignity:
Your grace covers me,
Your grace covers me, oh.

Saving grace, washing over me;
Saving grace, that made a way for me:
I was lost until You rescued me,
Your grace covers me.

I'm overwhelmed
By Your love and goodness,
I'm overwhelmed
That You took my brokenness:
Amazing love, how can this be?
Your grace covers me,
Your grace covers me.

1295 Sue Rinaldi, Caroline Bonnett & Steve Bassett
Copyright © 2001 Thankyou Music

I AM HELPLESSLY IN LOVE WITH YOU.
I am lost in something precious.
I am drowning in the sea of You.
I am found amongst Your treasures.

And I don't know why You give Yourself,
And I can't explain why You should care.
When all heaven sings Your glory,
I'm humbled that You hear my prayer.

I can only give my heart to You,
I can only give my heart.
(Repeat)

I am helplessly devoted to You;
I am scorched by strange new fire.
I am running deeper into You.
I am high upon the wire.

It's like breathing some strange new air,
Walking on some distant moon.
I'll sing a song from the depths of my soul:
Seeking, finding, coming home.
Seeking, finding, coming home.

1296 Brian Houston
Copyright © 2002 Thankyou Music

I AM THE ONE WITH THE UNCLEAN LIPS,
I am the one whose mind is jaded.
I am the one with the impure heart,
And all my innocence has faded.

Wash me clean in Your river of mercy.
Restore my soul by a clear blue stream.
Wash me clean in Your river of mercy,
Restore my soul, renew me again.

I am the one whose walk is faithless,
I am the one who walks away.
I am the one whose debts are many
And I am the one who cannot pay.

You are the Lord who is my fortress;
You are the Lord who is my hope.
You are the Lord who is my refuge,
The only safe place for my soul.

1297 Darlene Zschech
Copyright © 2001 Darlene Zschech/
Hillsong Publishing/Kingsway Music

I BEHOLD YOUR POWER AND GLORY,
Bring an offering, come before You;
Worship You, Lord,
In the beauty of Your holiness.
(Repeat)

Whenever I call, You're there,
Redeemer and Friend;
Cherished beyond all words,
This love never ends.
Morning by morning
Your mercy awakens my soul.

I lift up my eyes to see
The wonders of heaven
Opening over me,
Your goodness abounds;
You've taken my breath away
With Your irresistible love.

1298 James Taylor
Copyright © 1999 Thankyou Music

I BELIEVE in everything You do,
All You have to say.
I've come to realise You're the only way,
Oh, I believe in You.

I've received something in my life
Greater than before:
Your truth has set me free and I love You,
    Lord,
Oh, I believe in You.

Let the angels sing of the Lord's great
*   love,*
Well, it's shining down like the heavens
*   above.*
Let the nations bow to the living God
And know Your truth,
I believe in You.

I believe, I believe,
I believe, I believe in You.
(Repeat)

1299 Stuart Townend & Keith Getty
Copyright © 2003 Thankyou Music

I BELIEVE IN GOD THE FATHER,
Maker of heaven and earth.
I believe in Christ the Saviour,
Lord of all, Son of God.
Born to Mary, lived and suffered
At the hands of those He'd made.
Crucified, was dead and buried,
And descended to the grave.

I believe that Jesus rose again,
And ascended into heaven
Where He sits with God the Father,
And will come to judge all men.
I believe in God the Spirit,
In His church that stands forgiven;
Resurrection of the body,
And eternal life to come.

1300 Johnny Parks
Copyright © 2001 Thankyou Music

I CALL ON YOU, ALMIGHTY LORD;
I call on You, Almighty Lord.
I call on You, Almighty Lord;
I call on You, Almighty Lord.

I come to You and stand before Your throne.
I lift my voice in worship here once more.
You turned the darkness in me into light.
You took my blinded soul and gave me sight.
As I sank down to the depths You heard my
    cry,
You lifted me and taught me how to fly.
You promised me You're always here to stay,
So as I stand before You, Lord, I want to
    say...

The heavenly host are captured by the love
Of the One who laid His life down at the
    cross.
We lift the name of Jesus to the skies,
So all might see and know that there is life.
And where there's hatred let me bring Your
    love.
And where there's sorrow let me bring Your
    joy.
As I stand before You, will You lift Your face
And bring resurrection power to this place?

1301 Jim Bailey
Copyright © 1994 Thankyou Music

**I CAN DO ALL (ALL!), ALL (ALL!), ALL
    THINGS**
Through Christ who strengthens me.
I can do all (all!), all (all!), all things
Through Christ who strengthens me.

Go to school: all things.
Obey the rules: all things.
Keep my cool: all things
Through Christ who strengthens me.

Make new friends: all things.
Give and lend: all things.
Make amends: all things
Through Christ who strengthens me.

Pray and sing: all things.
Love our King: all things.
Everything: all things
Through Christ who strengthens me.

1302 Ken Riley
Copyright © 1995 McKenzie Music/
Adm. by Kingsway Music

I CAN FEEL YOUR ARMS surrounding,
Treasuring my soul.
Draw me ever closer into Your love,
Into Your love.
Lead me to Your place of wonder,
Shower me with grace.
Holy God, forgive my unrighteous ways,
Unrighteous ways.

Oh I love You, Lord,
All I am is Yours,
As Your mercy pours into my heart.
You're my faithful King,
Over everything,
Hear my spirit sing that Jesus is Lord.

1303 Ken Riley
Copyright © 1999 Thankyou Music

I COME AS I AM,
Baring all of my shame.
Surround me with love
And acceptance again.

> *Come closer, Lord,*
> *Come and restore;*
> *Come closer, Lord.*

Nothing I bring
Is too great to forgive,
Though each time Your grace
Is betrayed by my sin.

1304 Paul Oakley
Copyright © 2000 Thankyou Music

I COME RUNNING to You, Father,
Trying to find a secret place with You.
My soul crying out, just to hear Your voice,
Oh, I must have You.

I come running to You, Jesus,
I'm so hungry for Your truth.
I've found many treasures
Hidden in Your word,
But I must have You.

Only You, Lord, will I worship,
Only You will I serve.
And my hope lies in You, Lord,
Only You can make me whole.
And I will say 'I love You.'
Yes, I will sing to You, to You.

I come longing for You, Spirit,
So dry I need to know Your touch.
I know living waters deep within me,
But I must have more of You.

1305 Kate Simmonds
Copyright © 2002 Thankyou Music

I COME TO BOW DOWN,
I come to hear You speak.
I wait before You
Where deep can call to deep.

Be my life, be my all;
Heart and soul I seek You, Lord.

My heart will praise You;
In praises You dwell.
I long to be with You
And come away with You.

Wonder of heaven, joy of my heart;
Strength of my being, I love You.
Rock of salvation, love of my life;
God of all comfort, draw near.

Heart and soul I seek You, Lord;
Heart and soul I seek You, Lord.

1306 Matt Parker & Paul Oakley
Copyright © 1999 Thankyou Music

I COME TO YOU, Lord of all hope,
Giver of life, revive my soul.
I wait for You, Prince of all peace,
King of all love, draw near to me.
It feels sometimes like You're far away,
Yet I know You are with me.

And I know I cannot go from Your
    presence, O Lord,
But I need to feel You here with me.
What can I do just to draw near to You?
Oh, I need to know You here with me now.

Come to me now, Lord of my heart,
I need to know unfailing love.
Consuming flame, passion and power,
Come let Your fire burn in me now.
It feels sometimes like You're far away,
Yet I know You are with me.

And I know...

Where can I go just to find You, O God?
Oh, I long to feel You holding me.
Know that I seek You with all of my heart.
Oh, I need to find You here with me now.

1307 Louise & Nathan Fellingham
Copyright © 2001 Thankyou Music

I COME TO YOU, to sit at Your feet,
I hear You call, I'm longing to meet You.
I lift my face to You, and catch Your eye,
Oh how You satisfy.

Jesus, Your love surrounds me.
Jesus, Your love completes me.

Now looking closer, I see the scars,
Stories of love, You paid the greatest price,
So that I may have life.
Thank You, my Friend,
You're showing me once again.

There's nothing like it,
There's nothing like it,
There's nothing like the love of God.
(Repeat)

No longer searching, I've found the One,
Just touched the surface, only begun;
This love goes deeper
Than any I've known.

1308 Paul Booth
Copyright © 1998 Thankyou Music

I COME, WANTING JUST TO BE WITH YOU;
Today let me hear Your voice.
I come, wanting just to give to You,
To say, You are everything.

Don't ever let my heart grow cold,
Don't ever let me lose sight of Your truth.
Draw near that I may drink from eternal
    water.

You are the Fountain of all life,
You are the peace unto my soul.
You are the Way, the Truth, the Light;
Jesus, into Your arms I run.
You are the holy Son of God,
You gave up Your life to save my soul.
You have redeemed me through the cross;
Jesus, with thankfulness I come.

1309　Neil Bennetts
　　　　Copyright © 2001 Thankyou Music

**I COUNT AS NOTHING
EVERY EARTHLY TREASURE**, Jesus;
What You have shown me is that
You are the source of my life.
So what else can I do
But stay here?

Why would I look for
Any worldly pleasure, Jesus,
When I have all things in You?
And just a heartbeat away.
So what else can I do
But stay here with You?

　　*You're all that I need,
　　You're all that I need,
　　So here I'll stay
　　And give my praise to You.*

1310　Sydney Carter
　　　　Copyright © 1963 Stainer & Bell Ltd

'I DANCED IN THE MORNING when the world
　　was begun,
And I danced in the moon and the stars and
　　the sun,
And I came down from heaven and I danced
　　on the earth:
At Bethlehem I had My birth.

　　*'Dance, then, wherever you may be,
　　I am the Lord of the dance,' said He,
　　'And I'll lead you all, wherever you may
　　　be,
　　And I'll lead you all in the dance,' said He.*

'I danced for the scribe and the pharisee,
But they would not dance and they wouldn't
　　follow Me.
I danced for the fishermen, for James and
　　John –
They came with Me and the dance went on.

'I danced on the Sabbath and I cured the
　　lame;
The holy people said it was a shame.
They whipped and they stripped and they
　　hung Me on high,
And they left Me there on a cross to die.

'I danced on a Friday when the sky turned
　　black;
It's hard to dance with the devil on your back.
They buried My body and they thought I'd
　　gone,
But I am the dance, and I still go on.

'They cut Me down and I leapt up high;
I am the life that'll never, never die.
I'll live in you if you'll live in Me;
I am the Lord of the dance', said He.

1311　Noel & Tricia Richards & Wayne Drain
　　　　Copyright © 1998 Thankyou Music

I DON'T KNOW WHY, I can't see how
Your precious blood could cleanse me now;
When all this time I've lived a lie,
With no excuse, no alibi.

　　*All I know is I find mercy;
　　All my shame You take from me.
　　All I know, Your cross has power,
　　And the blood You shed cleanses me.*

It's way beyond what I can see,
How anyone could die for me.
So undeserved, this precious grace;
You've won my heart, I'll seek Your face.

1312　Bethan Stevens (Abundant Life Ministries,
　　　　Bradford, England)
　　　　Copyright © 2002 Thankyou Music

I ENTER IN before You now,
I come to You with an open heart.
I lift my voice to worship You,
I love You, Lord,
And I could stay in Your presence forever.

Lord God, I come before You
With my sacrifice of praise.
I am humbled in Your presence,
Jesus, Name above all names.

1313　Noel Richards & Wayne Drain
　　　　Copyright © 2001 Thankyou Music

IF I SEEK YOU, I will find You,
But I need to take the time.
If I call You, You will answer,
But I need to take the time.

　　*Give me a pure heart,
　　Give me a pure heart,
　　I'm calling to You.
　　Give me a pure heart,
　　Give me a pure heart,
　　I'm longing for You.*

If I listen, I will hear You,
But I need to take the time.
If I follow, You will lead me,
But I need to take the time.

1314 Matt Redman & Tom Lane
Copyright © 2002 Thankyou Music/
worshiptogether.com songs/The Bridge Worx/
Adm. by Kingsway Music

IF IT WASN'T FOR YOUR MERCY,
If it wasn't for Your love,
If it wasn't for Your kindness,
How could I stand?

If it wasn't for Your cleansing,
If it wasn't for Your blood,
If it wasn't for Your goodness,
How could I stand?

And yet I find myself again
Where even angels fear to tread,
Where I would never dare to come,
But for the cleansing of Your blood.

With You there is forgiveness,
And therefore You are feared.
Jesus, it's Your loving kindness
That brings me to my knees.

In the beauty of Your holiness. *(×4)*

1315 Ken Riley
Copyright © 1999 Thankyou Music

IF MY PEOPLE, who are called by My name,
Will humble themselves and pray,
And will seek My face,
And turn from their wicked ways.
(Repeat)

Then I will hear from heaven and forgive their
sin.
Yes, I will hear from heaven and forgive their
sin.
Yes, I will hear from heaven and forgive their
sin,
And will heal their land,
Yes, I will heal their land.

Will You hear from heaven and forgive my
sin?
Oh, will You hear from heaven and forgive
my sin?
Will You hear from heaven and forgive my
sin?
Oh, will You hear from heaven and forgive
my sin?

1316 David Lyle Morris & Faith Forster
Copyright © 2001 Thankyou Music

IF WE DIED WITH CHRIST,
We'll also live with Him,
And if we endure,
We'll also reign with Christ.
If we deny Him, He will disown us,
But if we're faithless,
Faithful He remains.

A faithful Saviour and unending in mercy
Is our God, the only true God.
The suffering Servant,
And our conquering Hero
Are You, God, forever true God.
You are worthy to receive our lives.
(Last time)
Cleansed from sin and alive to Christ.

If we please the Lord
In this present world,
We will inherit eternal life to come.
For He has promised
To raise us from the dead
If we walk worthily of Christ the risen One.

1317 Noel Richards & Wayne Drain
Copyright © 2001 Thankyou Music

I GIVE MY HEART TO WHAT I TREASURE;
My devotion, everything I am.
Like a diamond, You treat me like I'm
precious;
To be Yours is more than I deserve.

Jesus, You are my treasure;
Jesus, nothing less will do.
Jesus, I am Yours forever;
Jesus, I want to live for You.

We are a people holy to our Saviour;
For this moment He has gathered us
To bring hope and healing to the nations,
Till His name is known in all the earth.

1318 Noel & Tricia Richards
Copyright © 1998 Thankyou Music

I HAVE COME HOME,
I'm here again,
Worn feet and ragged heart.
Wasted my time,
Wandered from ways that are best.
I don't deserve from You
Mercy that falls anew every day:
All I want is You.

You know my name,
Call me Your friend,
You draw me to Your side.
Though I have failed,
Fallen so far, still You care.
Grace covers all my shame.
Jesus, You took the blame, this is love:
All I want is You.

I am restored,
Where I belong,
At one with You again.
With all my heart
I choose to walk in Your ways.
Held in Your strong embrace,
No one will take Your place in my heart:
All I want is You.

1319 Martin Cooper & Paul Oakley
Copyright © 1999 Thankyou Music

I HAVE COME TO LOVE YOU,
For You have won my heart
When You revealed Your love to me.
My life will be a witness
Of such love and such forgiveness,
For You have given me Your peace,
And You're everything I need.

> *I love to sing Your name,*
> *To speak about Your fame,*
> *You're worthy of my praise.*
> *I long to worship You*
> *In spirit and in truth,*
> *It's all I want to do.*

You have come to love me
And heal my broken heart,
Now I am reaching out to You.
Your strength is in my weakness,
I'm clinging to Your promise,
So let Your work in me shine through
In everything I do.

As I come before You now,
Let Your Spirit touch me;
I will make this gospel known.
Fill me with Your love and power
And Your compassion,
Through me let Your kingdom come.

1320 Andrew Rogers
Copyright © 2001 Thankyou Music

I HAVE COME TO REALISE
The glory of the Lord resides
In this jar of clay.
And if my world is going to see
The glory of the Lord revealed,
Then my pride must break.
Then the fragrance of Jesus
Will be released,
And the glory of God will be revealed
In all my world.

> *Jesus, let Your name*
> *Be fragrant in me,*
> *Like perfume that's poured*
> *From this vessel of clay.*
> (Repeat)

And I will live all my days
To be the praise,
And I will live all my days
To be the praise of Your glory.

1321 Matt Redman
Copyright © 2000 Thankyou Music

I HAVE HEARD SO MANY SONGS,
Listened to a thousand tongues,
But there is one that sounds above them all.
The Father's song, the Father's love,
You sung it over me and for eternity
It's written on my heart.

Heaven's perfect melody,
The Creator's symphony,
You are singing over me
The Father's song.
Heaven's perfect mystery,
The King of love has sent for me,
And now You're singing over me
The Father's song.

1322 Lex Loizides
Copyright © 2000 Thankyou Music

I HAVE HIS WORD,
His great and precious promises.
He took my sin, His righteousness is mine.
I am in Christ,
Secure for all eternity:
No power can sever me, nor cast me off
From His abundant, free
And sovereign love.

I have His word,
The Master Builder will succeed.
The gates of hell, they never will prevail.
Throughout the earth
The joy of Jesus is His church;
She is the mystery that stirred His heart,
Drawing Him out of heaven
To shed His blood.

I have His word,
A day is fixed when all the world
In sudden awe the Son of God shall see.
And in that day
Our eyes shall see His majesty;
What then of sufferings? What then of tears?
We shall see perfectly
When He appears!

I have His word
That every race shall reign with Him,
We'll reach our home, the new Jerusalem.
The Triune God
Shall dwell with man eternally,
More joys than eye has seen or ear has heard
Wait for us certainly,
I have His word.

1323
Tim Hughes
Copyright © 1998 Thankyou Music

I JUST WANT TO LOVE,
I just want to sing
To the One above
Who has touched this thirsty soul.
(Repeat)
And now I'll never be the same.

> *I'll always love You,*
> *I'll always sing to You, Jesus.*
> *I long to worship You in spirit and in truth.*
> (Repeat)

Every day I'll come,
Spend my life with You,
Learning of Your heart,
And what You're calling me to do.
(Repeat)
My every breath belongs to You.

And with this song
We'll lift the name of Jesus higher.
And with a shout
We'll raise up one voice.

1324
Reuben Morgan
Copyright © 1998 Reuben Morgan/
Hillsong Publishing/Kingsway Music

I KNOW HE RESCUED MY SOUL,
His blood has covered my sin,
I believe, I believe.
My shame He's taken away,
My pain is healed in His name,
I believe, I believe.
I'll raise a banner;
My Lord has conquered the grave.

> *My Redeemer lives, my Redeemer lives;*
> *My Redeemer lives, my Redeemer lives.*

You lift my burden, I'll rise with You:
I'm dancing on this mountain-top
To see Your kingdom come.

1325
D.W. Whittle (1840–1901) adapt. Stuart Townend
Copyright © 1999 Thankyou Music

I KNOW NOT WHY GOD'S WONDROUS GRACE
To me hath been made known;
Nor why, unworthy as I am,
He claimed me for His own.

I know not how this saving faith
To me He did impart;
Or how believing in His word
Wrought peace within my heart.

> *But I know whom I've believèd;*
> *He's able now to save*
> *What I've committed unto Him*
> *Until that final day.*

I know not how the Spirit moves,
Convincing men of sin;
Revealing Jesus through the word,
Creating faith in Him.

I know not what of good or ill
May be reserved for me,
Of weary ways or golden days
Before His face I see.

I know not when my Lord may come;
I know not how or where,
If I shall pass the vale of death,
Or meet Him in the air.

1326 David Gate
Copyright © 1999 Thankyou Music

I KNOW YOU LOVE AN OFFERING
That's costly, outreaching,
Touching Your heart for the poor.
The songs we sing as our offerings
Are more fragrant in Your presence,
If we live a life of love.

And as we follow Your heart,
We are led to the lost,
Finding there a place of praise,
No matter what the cost.
So we will stand with the weak,
Give our most to the least,
Serving You with all we have,
Your kingdom, God, we seek.

Now I see what You command:
Be faithful and humble,
Putting selfish hopes aside,
So change my heart that I may love
My neighbour as my brother,
And to live a life of love.

1327 Matt Redman
Copyright © 2000 Thankyou Music

I LIFT YOU HIGH, and bow down low,
How high can You be?
How low can I go?
I lift You high, and bow down low,
How high can You be?
How low can I go?
(First time only)
O Lord?

You must increase,
I must decrease, Lord.
I'll bow down,
And You will be adored.

1328 Gareth Robinson
Copyright © 2002 Thankyou Music

I LIVE MY LIFE TO WORSHIP YOU,
I spend my days serving You,
And now I come, I come.
I want to spend some time with You,
To steal away and be with You,
So now I come, I come.

Just to be with You,
Just to know more of Your love;
Just to be with You,
And to love You.

And here You know me,
And here You know me,
And here You know me,
And here I love You.

1329 John Ellis
Copyright © 1999 Thankyou Music

I LOVE YOU, LORD, I worship You,
I love You, Lord, always.
So thankful, Lord, You saved my life,
You saved my life, today.

Let me be a shining light for You,
Let me be a joy to You always.
Let me be a shining light for You,
Let me be a joy to You always.

And Lord, I love to bring to You
The honour due Your name;
Just look at what You've done for me,
I'll never be the same.

1330 Ken Riley
Copyright © 2001 Thankyou Music

I LOVE YOU MORE EACH DAY,
With all my heart can give;
Worship at Your feet,
Lost within Your gaze.
Just to know that You're near,
My treasure is here,
That You gave Your life
To save me;
How my heart sings with praise
And calls on Your name,
My Saviour, my Lover, my King,
Come to me again!

1331 Stuart Townend & J.K. Jamieson
Copyright © 2002 Thankyou Music

IMAGE OF INVISIBLE GOD,
Creator and Sustainer of all;
The King who came to ransom my soul,
Thank You for Your perfect love.

Holy One whom angels attend,
Righteous King who calls me His friend;
The Prince who offers peace without end,
Thank You for Your perfect love.

And it's You, O Lord,
You're all that I could ask for,
And in You, O Lord, I find the deepest joy:
Fountain of life, ocean of mercy and peace.
And it's You, O Lord,
Who gives me strength to follow,
And in You, O Lord, is grace for every day
Boundless in love,
Fullness of heaven on earth.

Therefore I will not be afraid,
Though mountains fall and rivers may rage;
I'm safe within the city You've made,
Thank You for Your perfect love.

1332 Brian Houston
Copyright © 2000 Thankyou Music

I'M CALLING OUT TO YOU,
There must be something more,
Some deeper place to find,
Some secret place to hide
Where I have not gone before.
Where my soul is satisfied,
And my sin is put to death,
And I can hear Your voice,
Your purpose is my choice,
As natural as a breath.

The love I knew before,
When You first touched my life,
I need You to restore,
I want You to revive.

Oh, place in my heart a passion for Jesus,
A hunger that seizes my passion for You.
My one desire, my greatest possession,
My only confession, my passion for You.

1333 Dave Bilbrough
Copyright © 2002 Thankyou Music

I'M CRADLED,
Cradled in the arms of love.
Yes, I'm cradled,
Cradled in the arms of love.

My struggles for approval
Were never meant to be.
To know that I'm accepted
Is Your desire for me.
Because…

My fears about the future,
All my anxieties,
Are calmed when I surrender
To the One who's holding me.

1334 Wayne Drain & Noel Richards
Copyright © 1998 Thankyou Music

I'M CRYING OUT, let everybody hear
This message loud and clear.
I'm crying out, I want the world to know
That Jesus is my hope.

I've chosen to believe
That God has chosen me
Now at this time.
He turned my life around,
I make a different sound,
Now I want to be a sign.
Harvest fields are white,
Wanna do what's right,
Can't keep it to myself,
Gotta go, gotta tell everyone, yeah.

1335 Geraldine Latty & Noel Robinson
Copyright © 2000 Thankyou Music

I'M DRAWN A LITTLE BIT CLOSER to You,
Hearing You whisper to me;
A little bit nearer to You,
Hearing the beat of Your heart.
Sensing Your power at work,
Seeing the need in Your world:
A little bit closer to You.

As I see Your faithfulness,
As I fix my eyes on You, O Lord;
As I run the race You've run,
Every day, every day.

1336 Ken Riley
Copyright © 2001 Thankyou Music

I MET YOU when You called my name,
Love surrounded and forgave,
And then You filled my heart with praise.
You are the Light that seeks to save:
A burning fire of purest grace,
Showering the world with love.

I will give glory unto You,
I will give glory unto You,
I give myself wholly, only to You.

You stand beside me when I fail,
And carry me through times of pain,
For You are with me all the way.
And when my life begins to fade
You'll be the lamp to guide my way,
Shining to eternity.

1337 Doug Horley
Copyright © 1999 Thankyou Music

I'M FOREVER IN YOUR LOVE,
I'm forever saved by grace.
You have chosen me
And crowned me with Your love.
I'll forever trust in You,
I'll forever say You're good.
You are King of kings
And I will worship You.

La la la la la la,
Just want to thank You,
La la la la la la,
Just want to praise You,
La la la la la la,
That I can live like this forever.
(Repeat)

1338

Marc James
Copyright © 2000 Vineyard Songs (UK/Eire)/
Adm. by CopyCare

I'M GIVING YOU MY HEART,
And all that is within,
I lay it all down
For the sake of You, my King.
I'm giving You my dreams,
I'm laying down my rights,
I'm giving up my pride
For the promise of new life.

> *And I surrender all to You, all to You.*
> *And I surrender all to You, all to You.*

I'm singing You this song,
I'm waiting at the cross,
And all the world holds dear,
I count it all as loss.
For the sake of knowing You,
The glory of Your name,
To know the lasting joy,
Even sharing in Your pain.

1339

Steve Earl
Copyright © 1998 PDI Worship/
Adm. by CopyCare

I'M GONNA TRUST IN GOD,
I'm gonna trust in Jesus
Without shame and without fear.
I'm gonna fix my eyes
On the hope of glory,
For His day is drawing near.

> *How great is the love of God,*
> *How steady is His hand*
> *To guide me through this world.*
> *And though I am weak, in Him I stand,*
> *And you will hear me say today,*
> *In faith, I'm gonna trust in God.*

Now when the cares of life
Seem overwhelming,
And my heart is sinking down,
I'm gonna lift my hands
To the One who'll help me,
To the One who holds my crown.

1340

Johnny Parks
Copyright © 2001 Thankyou Music

I'M GRATEFUL for the way You look at me.
I'm thankful that You don't give up.
You're a friend who's smiled at me a
thousand times.
When I cause You pain, You bring me love.

I've found a place where I'm free.
I'm dancing now, 'cause You love me.
(You love me, You love me, You love me.)

> *I love You, You know it's true.*
> *And all I want is to be close to You.*

When I've done the worst,
You've seen the best in me.
I was running away,
But You brought some rest to me.
My heart is Yours and I give it all to You.
And when it's tough, I know You'll
Pull me through.

1341

Paul Oakley
Copyright © 1998 Thankyou Music

I'M LEARNING TO LOVE YOU,
To love and to trust You.
I'm learning to give You all that I am.
I'm learning to cling to the words You have
spoken.
I'm learning to let go my life in Your hands.

For You are faithful in all of Your ways,
In wisdom unsearchable, and full of grace.
Oh, You are beautiful beyond words.
I'm learning to love You.

So teach me to love You,
To love and to trust You,
And teach me to give You all that I am.
And teach me to cling to the words You have
spoken,
Teach me to let go my life in Your hands.

We are like shadows that change with the
day;
And like the flowers our beauty will fade.
But Yours is the kingdom and the power;
Forever and ever Your glory will always
remain.

1342 Matt Redman
Copyright © 2001 Thankyou Music

I'M MAKING MELODY in my heart to You.
I'm making melody in my heart to You.
Pouring out Your praise
With everything within.
I'm making melody in my heart to You.
I'm making melody in my heart to You.
Yours will always be
The song I love to sing.

How can hearts not love Your name?
How can souls not sing Your praise?
Jesus, You put music in my soul.

1343 Dave Bilbrough
Copyright © 2000 Thankyou Music

I'M ON MY KNEES at the cross,
Where Your blood was sacrificed;
So amazed that there is grace
Enough for me.
I don't deserve the love You bring,
But I'm at that place again,
Where I need You
To forgive my foolish heart.

Oh, what mercy,
Oh, what mercy,
Oh, what mercy
Is mine to receive.

1344 Jim Bailey
Copyright © 1994 Thankyou Music

I'M WORKING OUT WHAT IT MEANS to
follow Jesus,
Adding up what it costs to follow Him;
Counting the times that His love is multiplying,
Realising He took away my sin.
He's always in my memory;
He'll never cancel what He's done for me.
When I add it together I calculate
Jesus is great, Jesus is great!

1345 Reuben Morgan
Copyright © 1999 Reuben Morgan/
Hillsong Publishing/Kingsway Music

IN AWE OF YOU, we worship
And stand amazed at Your great love.
We're changed from glory to glory,
We set our hearts on You, our God.

Now Your presence fills this place,
Be exalted in our praise.
As we worship I believe
You are near.
(Repeat)

Blessing and honour
And glory and power
Forever, forever.
(Repeat)

1346 Stuart Townend & Keith Getty
Copyright © 2001 Thankyou Music

IN CHRIST ALONE my hope is found,
He is my light, my strength, my song;
This Cornerstone, this solid Ground,
Firm through the fiercest drought and storm.
What heights of love, what depths of peace,
When fears are stilled, when strivings cease!
My Comforter, my All in All,
Here in the love of Christ I stand.

In Christ alone! – who took on flesh,
Fullness of God in helpless babe!
This gift of love and righteousness,
Scorned by the ones He came to save:
Till on that cross as Jesus died,
The wrath of God was satisfied –
For every sin on Him was laid;
Here in the death of Christ I live.

There in the ground His body lay,
Light of the world by darkness slain:
Then bursting forth in glorious Day
Up from the grave He rose again!
And as He stands in victory
Sin's curse has lost its grip on me,
For I am His and He is mine –
Bought with the precious blood of Christ.

No guilt in life, no fear in death,
This is the power of Christ in me;
From life's first cry to final breath,
Jesus commands my destiny.
No power of hell, no scheme of man,
Can ever pluck me from His hand;
Till He returns or calls me home,
Here in the power of Christ I'll stand!

1347 Paul Oakley & Martin Cooper
Copyright © 2002 Thankyou Music

I NEED YOU like the summer needs the sun.
I need You to walk and to run.
I need You like a river needs the rain.
I need You to fill me again.
Without You I run dry;
Without You I won't even survive.

So wake me, take me with You,
Chase me where Your river runs,
Romance me till my heart belongs to You.
Oh, draw me closer to You,
Lead me in Your ways,
Enchant me 'cause my life belongs to You.

I need You like the stars need the sky.
I need You to help me to shine.
I need You like a singer needs a song.
I need You to carry on.
Without You I run dry,
Without You I won't even survive.

Embrace me, let me feel Your strength,
Hide me in Your shade,
You're my shelter in the rain.

1348   Paul Oakley
Copyright © 1998 Thankyou Music

I NEED YOU NOW,
My King, my Love;
I am more aware this clay
Than all Your power within.
I wait for You,
My Hope, my Love,
Because I've dreamed I'd see
Your kingdom come and I still believe.

So come and breathe on me now,
I am poured out for You.
Come and release Your power.
I'm crying out to You,
I'm crying out to You.

What works have I?
What fruit to show?
I can hardly stand before Your grace,
Yet I, I know
Your love, Your grace
Has lifted me,
But I need You now so I can build
With gold, pure gold.

Your promise alone
Should be enough for me.
Still I'm crying out,
'I need Your touch.'

1349   Kate Simmonds & Stuart Townend
Copyright © 2001 Thankyou Music

IN EVERY DAY THAT DAWNS,
I see the light of Your splendour around me;
And everywhere I turn,
I know the gift of Your favour upon me.
What can I do but give You glory, Lord?
Everything good has come from You.

I'm grateful for the air I breathe,
I'm so thankful for this life I live,
For the mercies that You pour on me,
And the blessings that meet every need.
And the grace that is changing me
From a hopeless case to a child that's free,
Free to give You praise,
For in everything
I know You love me.
I know You love me.

Through all that I have known,
I have been held in the shelter of Your hand;
And as my life unfolds,
You are revealing the wisdom
Of Your sovereign plan.
There are no shadows in Your faithfulness,
There are no limits to Your love.

1350   Polish traditional carol
tr. Edith M.G. Reed (1885–1933)
Copyright Control

INFANT HOLY, Infant lowly,
For His bed a cattle stall;
Oxen lowing, little knowing,
Christ the babe is Lord of all.
Swift are winging angels singing,
Nowells ringing, tidings bringing:
Christ the babe is Lord of all;
Christ the babe is Lord of all.

Flocks were sleeping, shepherds keeping
Vigil till the morning new;
Saw the glory, heard the story,
Tidings of a gospel true.
Thus rejoicing, free from sorrow,
Praises voicing, greet the morrow:
Christ the babe was born for you!
Christ the babe was born for you!

1351   Paul Oakley
Copyright © 1999 Thankyou Music

IN THE SHADOW OF THE CROSS,
Let everything fall into place again.
Jesus Christ, my sacrifice,
How I need to find Your grace again.

And nothing I can do
Could add to all You've done,
So let my soul be satisfied.
As I receive Your favour,
I will overcome.
So in my life be glorified.

Jesus Christ, my perfect Priest,
How You understand my weaknesses.
Thank You for Your gift to me:
Through Your sufferings I now
Possess this peace.

1352

IN THIS PLACE WE GATHER
To worship You together,
To come before You, holy God.
(Repeat)

And as we seek Your face,
Let this be Your dwelling place,
We have come to worship You.
We come to give our all,
It's at Your feet we fall,
We have come to praise You.

We have come to worship,
We have come to worship,
We have come to worship You.

1353

IN THIS STILLNESS I will worship,
Love You, Jesus,
I turn toward to kiss Your face.
I come running, thirsting, longing
For You, Jesus,
In the quiet of this place.
Draw me closer to You, Jesus,
I would be with You.

Risen Healer, conquering Saviour,
King of kings and Prince of Peace.
Faithful Father, my Friend forever,
I will live to bring You praise.

In Your presence I will bow down,
Join with the angels
Singing 'Holy is Your name'.
In this moment heaven's fragrance
Touches earth and
I can feel Your kingdom come.
Draw me closer to You, Jesus,
I would be with You.

1354

IN YOUR ARMS OF LOVE I SING,
Giving glory to my King:
I have come to seek Your face
In this secret, secret place.
And I will bow before Your throne,
For my life is not my own.

And I will praise You,
Every day I'll come before Your throne.
I am holy unto You.
And I will give You
All my hopes, my dreams I lay them
*   down.*
Lord, may I be found in You.

I have taken up my cross,
What was gain I've counted loss.
Father, let Your will be done
For I am broken by this love.
Send Your fire to purify,
Jesus, teach me how to die.

And I will follow You, my Lord,
Forevermore and ever more,
And I will follow You, my Lord,
Forevermore.
(Repeat)

1355

IN YOUR PRESENCE there is fullness of life,
And healing flowing for body, soul and mind.
God of miracles, God of the impossible is
   here,
God is here.

God is here, let the broken-hearted
*   rejoice.*
God is here, let the sick say 'I am well.'
God is here, let the weak say 'I am strong.'
God is here, His wonders to perform.

In Your presence there is perfect peace;
In the stillness I behold Your deity.
God of wonder, God of power is here,
God is here.

Oh, His wonders, yes, His wonders,
His wonders to perform.
Oh, His wonders, yes, His wonders,
His wonders to perform.
(Repeat)

1356

IN YOUR PRESENCE THERE IS JOY,
In Your presence there is freedom,
But the greatest joy of all
Is to know we've made You smile.
In Your presence there is life,
In Your presence there is healing,
But the greatest joy of all
Is to know we've reached Your heart.

God of glory, we give You praise,
Lift You up in this holy place;
Our hearts are ready, our lives made new,
It's all we long to do.
God of glory, we give You praise,
We lift You up in this holy place;
Our hearts are ready, our lives made new,
God of glory, we worship You.

1357 Graham Kendrick
Copyright © 2002 Make Way Music

IN YOU WE LIVE, Jesus,
In You we move.
In You we breathe, Jesus,
In You we love.
And we are Your body here,
We are Your body here.

Your touch – our hands,
Your words – our voice,
Your way – our feet,
Your tears in our eyes,
Your Spirit is here.

You give – we share,
You lead – we go,
You send – we serve,
You build and we grow.
Your Spirit is here.

Across the world, You're moving;
The sound of prayer is growing stronger,
From every tribe and nation
Joining in one salvation song.

You are the light that's dawning,
You are the hope transforming all things;
Freeing the whole creation
To join in one salvation song,
One song.

1358 Judy Bailey
Copyright © 1993 Daybreak Music Ltd

I REACH UP HIGH, I touch the ground,
I stomp my feet and turn around.
I've to (woo woo) praise the Lord.
I jump and dance with all my might,
I might look funny, but that's all right,
I've got to (woo woo) praise the Lord.

I'll do anything just for my God
'Cause He's done everything for me.
It doesn't matter who is looking on,
Jesus is the person that I want to please.

May my whole life be a song of praise,
To worship God in every way.
In this song the actions praise His name,
I want my actions every day to do the same.

1359 Paul Oakley
Copyright © 1999 Thankyou Music

I SEE THE LORD,
And He is high and lifted up,
And His train fills the temple.
I see You, Lord,
And You are high and lifted up,
And Your train fills the temple.

And I cry holy, holy is the Lord,
Holy is the Lord most high.
And I cry holy, holy is the Lord,
Holy, is the Lord most high.

I see Your holiness,
And light surrounds Your throne;
Who am I to come before You?
But now my guilt is gone,
My sins are washed away,
Through Your blood I come.

Who am I that I should gain the Father's love?
Now my eyes have seen the King.
Touch my lips that I may tell of all You've
    done:
Fill my heart I cry,
Be glorified!

1360 Michael Sandeman
Copyright © 2001 Thankyou Music

I SEE YOU HANGING THERE,
Nailed to a splintered wooden beam,
Drinking pain and sorrows,
Breathing agony.
And in those dark, dark hours,
As life drained from Your flesh and bones,
I know my life had its beginning at Your
    cross.
And I thank You, thank You:

For the cross, where You bled,
For the cross, where You died,
For the cross,
Where You've broken Satan's back.
For the cross, where You won,
For the cross of victory,
For the cross,
Where You paid the price for me.

You were my substitute
In laying down Your life for mine,
Being cursed and bearing
The wrath of God for me.
You were crushed by sin,
Your punishment has brought me peace,
And by the wounds You suffered
I'm alive and healed.
And I thank You, thank You:

Two days in the grave,
Then You rose up from the dead –
Now You reign in glory,
Rule in righteousness.
And I was raised with You,
Free at last from all my sin,
Safe forever in the shelter of my King.
And I thank You, thank You:

1361 Ken Riley
Copyright © 1999 Thankyou Music

I THANK YOU FOR THE CROSS
Where all my shame was laid,
Broken by Your power,
Banished to the grave.
You gave Yourself for me,
A sinner for a King,
Offering Your death
And suffering my sin.

And I will give my life
To You, Lord,
For with grace You came
To pay the ransom for my soul.
And I will live my life
For You, Lord.
You brought me back from death,
Into Your mercy on the cross.

1362 Dan Adler
Copyright © 1999 Heart of the City Music/
Word Music Inc./Adm. by CopyCare

IT IS GOOD, it is good,
It is good to give thanks to the Lord on
high,
To sing of Your faithfulness
And loving kindness both day and night;
To play on our instruments
Sweet songs of praise for the things You
do:
It is good, it is good,
It is good to give thanks to You.

For though the wicked
Spring up like the grass and are everywhere,
Soon they will perish;
But all those planted in Your house
Will grow without end.
Sing it again!

For though we struggle
And trials and troubles still come our way,
You won't forsake us;
Your word has told us
Your promises will never end.
Sing it again!

(Leader – All)
Why give Him praise? (Because He is
worthy.)
Why should we sing? (He loves you and me.)
Why give Him thanks? (Because He forgave
us.)
Why celebrate? (Because we are free.)
And when should we thank Him? (In morning
and evening.)
In what circumstance? (The good and the bad.)
Is it always easy? (No, it's not so easy.)
But is it good? (Yes, it's good, it is good, it is
good.)

1363 Duke Kerr
Copyright © 1995 Remission Music UK/
Adm. by Sovereign Music UK

IT IS TO YOU I give the glory,
It is to You I give the praise.
Because You have done so much for me,
I will magnify Your name.
It is to You, holy Father,
No one else but You,
And I will praise Your name,
Praise Your name,
And I will praise Your name forevermore.

1364 Rohn Bailey
Copyright © 1999 Thankyou Music

I TREMBLE IN YOUR PRESENCE,
I am humbled that You came,
Yet I know it's all because I choose to praise
You.
I recognise Your fragrance,
As Your glory fills this place;
All I'd planned to say means nothing now.

Oh, how I long for You.
Oh, how I long for You.
Oh, how I long for You, oh.

I shiver in Your presence,
I am frozen by my shame.
My heart is breaking more than I can stand it.
Your radiance is blinding,
Yet You hug me like a friend,
I am overcome by Your mercy again.

1365 Joy Webb
Copyright © Salvationist Publishing &
Supplies Ltd/Adm. by CopyCare

IT WAS ON A STARRY NIGHT when the hills
were bright,
Earth lay sleeping, sleeping calm and still;
Then in a cattle shed, in a manger bed
A boy was born, King of all the world.

And all the angels sang for Him,
The bells of heaven rang for Him;
For a boy was born, King of all the world.
(Repeat)

Soon the shepherds came that way, where
the baby lay,
And were kneeling, kneeling by His side.
And their hearts believed again, for the peace
of men;
For a boy was born, King of all the world.

1366 Tim Beck
Copyright © 1999 Thankyou Music

I'VE COME TO MEET WITH YOU, my God,
To bless Your heart, my King;
To be with You, to know Your love,
To give an offering.

And I will seek Your lovely face,
Through the veil I'll come,
To love You in Your dwelling place,
To gaze upon Your throne.
(Repeat)

Your grace and love have come to me,
You've set this captive free.
This child is Yours, You have redeemed
For life eternally.

I know the punishment You took for me;
Thank You, Saviour, for the cost,
That set me free,
That set me free.

1367 David Gate
Copyright © 2001 Thankyou Music

I'VE FILLED MY DAYS WITH DETAILS
And all the choices of the earth,
Carried the yoke of worry,
And all the burdens that it brings.
And through the midst of all the rushing,
You whisper to our hearts,
And with Your sweet voice
You say to us:

To be still and know You are God,
To be still and know You are God,
Just to rest in Your arms.

So give me peace and wisdom
To know how to fill my time,
Where I can learn to keep You
At the centre of my life.
So through the midst of all the rushing
There is time to spend with You,
And my foundation
Will daily be:

1368 Matt Redman
Copyright © 2000 Thankyou Music

I'VE THROWN IT ALL AWAY
That I might gain a life in You.
I've found all else is loss
Compared to the joys of knowing You.
Your beauty and Your majesty
Are far beyond compare:
You've won my heart,
Now this will be my prayer.

'Take the world but give me Jesus!'
You're the treasure in this life.
'Take the world but give me Jesus!'
Is my cry.
Now I've seen You as the Saviour,
I will leave the rest behind:
'Take the world but give me Jesus!'
Is my cry.

Into the world I'll go
That I might live this life of love.
I won't be overcome,
For You are in me and You are strong.
For time and for eternity
I know I'm in Your care;
You've won my heart,
Now this will be my prayer.

1369 Paul Oakley
Copyright © 2000 Thankyou Music

I WANT TO BE BEFORE YOUR THRONE,
Where Your glory shines.
I want to see, I want to know
The One who saved my life.

I want to know the One who shines,
The One enthroned above the skies,
The One who gave His life,
Was crucified, and lifted up on high.

I want to know as I am known
In this space and time.
Now I am Yours, and in lover's words:
Jesus, You are mine.

In You I live, in You I move
And have my being.
It's You I love,
It's You I choose to believe in.

1370

I WILL CALL UPON THE NAME OF THE LORD,
For He is worthy to be praised.
I will shout hosanna to Jesus, my Rock.
(First time)
I believe He is the Mighty One who saves.

(Second time)
I believe He is the Mighty One,
The Mighty One who saves.

> *God of the breakthrough,*
> *God of the breakthrough,*
> *All things are possible with You.*
> *(Lord, I believe You are the)*
> *God of the breakthrough,*
> *God of the breakthrough.*
> *Let Your love shine down on me.*

Let Your love shine down on me. *(×4)*

I will call on Your name, O Lord. *(×4)*
Jesus!

Jehovah Elohim, the Lord is God.
Jehovah Nissi, the Lord is my banner.
Jehovah Rophi, He is the Lord who heals me.
Jehovah Jireh, the Lord who provides.
Jehovah Tsidkenu, the Lord, our
  righteousness.
Jehovah Shalom, He is the Lord of peace.
Jehovah Rohi, the Lord is my Shepherd.
Jehovah Shammah, the Lord is here.

1371

I WILL COME, come, come to the waters and
  drink;
I will praise, praise, praise Your name again.
I will rest, rest, rest, rest at Your feet,
For You have won my heart once again.

I will thirst, thirst, thirst for all that You give;
And I will fall, fall, fall, fall into Your arms again.
I will call, call, call to You alone each day,
For You have won my heart once again.

> *And You are God,*
> *With fire in Your eyes,*
> *And You are God,*
> *Adorned in radiant light.*
> *You are God*
> *Whose hands were pierced for all:*
> *What choice do I have,*
> *But to give You my very all?*

I shall wait, wait, wait at the cross where we
  meet;
And I will live, live, live, by Your name I speak.
I will run, run, run for Your face to seek,
For You have won my heart once again.

1372

I WILL ENTER YOUR HOUSE with
  thanksgiving,
I will sing of Your goodness to me.
For my heart is eternally grateful,
I am blessed abundantly.

You have given me life in all its fullness,
And joy no words can describe.
But I know it's for more than me,
It's for those, those You sent me to reach.

> *I am blessed, blessed to be a blessing,*
> *I am blessed, I live under an open heaven,*
> *Blessed, that all may see*
> *It's Christ, Christ in me.*
> (Repeat)

1373

I WILL LOVE YOU FOR THE CROSS,
And I will love You for the cost:
Man of sufferings,
Bringer of my peace.
You came into a world of shame,
And paid the price we could not pay:
Death that brought me life,
Blood that brought me home.
Death that brought me life,
Blood that brought me home.

> *And I love You for the cross,*
> *I'm overwhelmed by the mystery.*
> *I love You for the cost,*
> *That Jesus, You would do this for me.*
> *When You were broken, You were beaten,*
> *You were punished, I go free.*
> *When You were wounded and rejected,*
> *In Your mercy, I am healed.*

Jesus Christ, the sinner's friend;
Does this kindness know no bounds?
With Your precious blood
You have purchased me.
O the mystery of the cross,
You were punished, You were crushed;
But that punishment
Has become my peace.
Yes, that punishment
Has become my peace.

1374 Ian Hannah
Copyright © 2001 Thankyou Music

I WILL NEVER BE THE SAME
Now my eyes are open wide.
I have been forever changed
Through the power of His blood.

I will triumph in the cross
That my Saviour bore for me.
I will stand with confidence
Because of Jesus.
I no longer fear the grave,
I'm a child of His grace.
I no longer feel ashamed,
Because of Jesus.

1375 Paul Oakley & J.K. Jamieson
Copyright © 1998 Thankyou Music

I WILL NEVER BE THE SAME,
Now that I have seen the cross;
And how You took upon Yourself
The fullness of the wrath of God.
And I may never understand
Just what You suffered in my place;
Jesus, You who knew no sin,
How You were made sin for us.

And oh, how fierce the Father's anger.
And though You were pierced,
All the pain could not compare;
So dark was the hour,
When all heaven turned its face away,
Turned its face away from You.
But how sweet is Your mercy
As it finds its way to me.

1376 Jennifer Atkinson & Robin Mark
Copyright © 1991 Authentic Publishing/
Adm. by CopyCare

JESUS, ALL FOR JESUS;
All I am and have and ever hope to be.
Jesus, all for Jesus;
All I am and have and ever hope to be.

All of my ambitions, hopes and plans,
I surrender these into Your hands.
All of my ambitions, hopes and plans,
I surrender these into Your hands.

> *For it's only in Your will that I am free.*
> *For it's only in Your will that I am free.*
> *Jesus, all for Jesus;*
> *All I am and have and ever hope to be.*

1377 Michael Frye
Copyright © 1999 Vineyard Songs (UK/Eire)/
Adm. by CopyCare

JESUS, BE THE CENTRE,
Be my source, be my light,
Jesus.

Jesus, be the Centre,
Be my hope, be my song,
Jesus.

> *Be the fire in my heart,*
> *Be the wind in these sails;*
> *Be the reason that I live,*
> *Jesus, Jesus.*

Jesus, be my vision,
Be my path, be my guide,
Jesus.

1378 Noel Richards
Copyright © 2001 Thankyou Music

JESUS CHRIST,
You came into this world to rescue me.
On the cross,
My sin was laid on You, what agony.
There Your precious life-blood flowed so free.
Every drop that fell still cleanses me.

> *All Your love* (×4)
> *Pouring out for me like a flood.*

I am safe
Upon the ocean of Your mercy.
I am loved
With all the passion of eternity.
It is deeper than the deepest sea;
Like a tidal wave it carries me.

> *All Your love* (×4)
> *Sweeping over me like a flood.*

So I stand
Upon Your promise of eternal grace.
I believe
That I will one day see You face to face.
I will worship You forevermore
In ways I never have before.

> *All my love* (×4)
> *Flowing out to You like a flood.*

1379 Martyn Layzell
Copyright © 2001 Thankyou Music

JESUS CHRIST, EMMANUEL,
The Saviour of the world;
Creator of the universe,
The true and living Word.
Let every tongue confess Your name,
And bow the knee before Your hand of grace,
Giving You the highest praise.

You are, You are the everlasting Prince of
Peace,
The First, the Last in whom all things were
made.
You reign with love, Counsellor, Almighty
God.
Jesus, You're the Name by which we're
saved,
Jesus, You're the Name above all names.

Holy One upon the throne,
To You the angels sing.
And here we join their heavenly song,
Proclaiming You as King.
Let every tongue confess Your name,
We bow the knee before Your hand of grace,
Giving You the highest praise.

1380 Nathan Fellingham
Copyright © 2002 Thankyou Music

JESUS CHRIST, HOLY ONE,
The lifter of our heads,
Through You I come, conquering Son,
To my Father in heaven.
And I'm confident that I belong to You,
As the Spirit testifies.
I shall not fear, fear has no hold,
So I cry 'Abba Father!'

What mercies You have poured on me,
With thankfulness I'll sing;
I choose to fix my mind
On all the blessings You have given me.
For You've revealed to me Your grace,
The wonder of the cross;
You've breathed new life to me,
And in Your victory I now stand today.

1381 John L. Bell & Graham Maule
Copyright © 1998 WGRG, Iona Community

JESUS CHRIST IS WAITING, waiting in the
streets;
No one is His neighbour, all alone He eats.
Listen, Lord Jesus, I am lonely too:
Make me, friend or stranger, fit to wait on
You.

Jesus Christ is raging, raging in the streets,
Where injustice spirals and real hope retreats.
Listen, Lord Jesus, I am angry too:
In the kingdom's causes, let me rage with
You.

Jesus Christ is healing, healing in the streets,
Curing those who suffer, touching those He
greets.
Listen, Lord Jesus, I have pity too:
Let my care be active, healing just like You.

Jesus Christ is dancing, dancing in the
streets,
Where each sign of hatred He, with love,
defeats.
Listen, Lord Jesus, I should triumph too:
Where good conquers evil, let me dance with
You.

Jesus Christ is calling, calling in the streets:
'Who will join My journey? I will guide their
feet.'
Listen, Lord Jesus, let my fears be few:
Walk one step before me; I will follow You.

1382 Margaret Becker & Keith Getty
Copyright © 2001 Modern M. Music/
Adm. by CopyCare/& Thankyou Music

JESUS, DRAW ME EVER NEARER,
As I labour through the storm.
You have called me to this passage,
And I'll follow, though I'm worn.

May this journey bring a blessing,
May I rise on wings of faith:
And at the end of my heart's testing,
With Your likeness let me wake.

Jesus, guide me through the tempest,
Keep my spirit staid and sure.
When the midnight meets the morning,
Let me love You even more.

Let the treasures of the trial
Form within me as I go.
And at the end of this long passage,
Let me leave them at Your throne.

1383 Geoff Bullock
Copyright © 1995 Word Music Inc./
Maranatha! Music/Adm. by CopyCare

JESUS, GOD'S RIGHTEOUSNESS
REVEALED,
The Son of Man, the Son of God, His
kingdom comes.
Jesus, redemption's sacrifice,
Now glorified, now justified, His kingdom
comes.

And His kingdom will know no end,
And its glory shall know no bounds,
For the majesty and power
Of this kingdom's King has come.
And this kingdom's reign,
And this kingdom's rule,
And this kingdom's power and authority,
Jesus, God's righteousness revealed.

Jesus, the expression of God's love,
The grace of God, the Word of God, revealed
  to us;
Jesus, God's holiness displayed,
Now glorified, now justified, His kingdom
  comes.

1384 Philip Lawson Johnston
Copyright © 1997 Thankyou Music

JESUS, HIGH KING OF HEAVEN,
We bring our high praise to You.
Jesus, high King of heaven,
To whom all high praise is due.

Who can be compared to You, O Holy One?
None in heaven or earth is Your equal.
You will not share Your glory with another;
Honour to Your name.

O Lord God Almighty, who is like You?
Yesterday, today and forever,
Power, mercy, faithfulness surround You;
Eternal is Your name.

You are the image, the radiance of God's
  glory.
Through You the universe was made.
You are the Alpha, Omega, the First and Last,
You are the Beginning and the End

1385 Brian Doerksen
Copyright © 2002 Integrity's Hosanna! Music/
Sovereign Music UK

JESUS, HOPE OF THE NATIONS;
Jesus, comfort for all who mourn,
You are the source
Of heaven's hope on earth.

Jesus, light in the darkness,
Jesus, truth in each circumstance,
You are the source
Of heaven's light on earth.

In history, You lived and died,
You broke the chains, You rose to life.

You are the Hope, living in us,
You are the Rock, in whom we trust.
You are the Light,
Shining for all the world to see.
You rose from the dead, conquering fear,
Our Prince of Peace, drawing us near.
Jesus, our Hope,
Living for all who will receive,
Lord, we believe.

1386 Alan Rose
Copyright © 1999 Thankyou Music

JESUS IS EXALTED to the highest place,
Seated at the right hand of our God.
He reigns in power and glory,
He is God's appointed heir,
He is righteous, He is holy, He is Lord!

Hallelujah! He is King of kings.
Hallelujah! He is the Lord.
Hallelujah! He is Jesus Christ,
Reigning forevermore, ever more.

The throne of God will last for all eternity,
We will reign with Him as those He has
  redeemed.
For we are a chosen people,
We will be the bride of Christ,
He has chosen us to ever be with Him!

The day is coming when He will appear,
His glory shining like the sun;
And every nation then will see and fear
The mighty and exalted One.

So let us throw aside all that would hinder us,
And run as those who run to win the prize.
For we will see His glory,
We will see Him face to face,
We will join Him as His glory fills the skies!

1387 Stuart Townend & Keith Getty
Copyright © 2003 Thankyou Music

'JESUS IS LORD' – the cry that echoes
  through creation;
Resplendent power, eternal Word, our Rock.
The Son of God, the King whose glory fills
  the heavens,
Yet bids us come to taste this living Bread.

Jesus is Lord – whose voice sustains the stars
  and planets,
Yet in His wisdom laid aside His crown.
Jesus the Man, who washed our feet, who
  bore our suffering,
Became a curse to bring salvation's plan.

Jesus is Lord – the tomb is gloriously empty!
Not even death could crush this King of love!
The price is paid, the chains are loosed, and
we're forgiven,
And we can run into the arms of God.

'Jesus is Lord' – a shout of joy, a cry of
anguish,
As He returns, and every knee bows low.
Then every eye and every heart will see His
glory,
The Judge of all will take His children home.

1388 David Fellingham
Copyright © 1998 Thankyou Music

JESUS, JESUS, HEALER, SAVIOUR,
Strong Deliverer,
How I love You,
How I love You.

1389 Dave Bilbrough
Copyright © 2000 Thankyou Music

JESUS, JESUS, JESUS,
How I love Your name.

The sweetest name on earth
Will never be enough
To tell the wonder of Your love.
Come hide me in Your arms
And calm my restless heart;
I hunger, Lord, for more of You.

1390 David Lyle Morris & Faith Forster
Copyright © 2000 Thankyou Music

JESUS, KING OF THE AGES,
*Pleading our cause before the throne of
God.
Jesus, the living Word of God,
Our Prophet, Priest and King,
Our Prophet, Priest and King.*

From the start You were there, Word of God,
Ancient promises You came to fulfil;
You came revealing the Father's heart,
His favour, His purpose, His will:
Sharing His good news with the poor,
Declaring God's kingdom is here.

At the cross You poured out costly blood,
Perfect sacrifice, atoning for sin,
So we may enter the holy place
To meet You, our faithful High Priest;
As we come to the mercy seat
We find grace in our time of need.

Jesus shall reign at the Father's hand
Till all of His enemies cease:
Hell and destruction, disease and death
Are under His glorious feet.

We will reign with Christ, *(echo)*
We will reign with Christ, *(echo)*
We will reign with Christ *(echo)*
Forever.

1391 Mike Sandeman
Copyright © 1999 Thankyou Music

JESUS LOVES THE CHURCH,
He gave Himself for His bride.
He knows what we will be,
A conquering army,
An unblemished people.
We're accepted, we're forgiven,
We're united with Him;
Not rejected, not forgotten,
Not abandoned in sin.

> *Can you hear Him singing,
> 'I love you, I love you'?
> Can you hear Him calling,
> 'I want you, I have chosen you to be
> Mine'?*

Jesus loves the church,
His passion through the ages.
Hell will not prevail.
He builds us together,
A living temple.
We're accepted, we're forgiven,
We're united with Him;
Not rejected, not forgotten,
Not abandoned in sin.

1392 Caroline Bonnett & Steve Bassett
Copyright © 2001 Thankyou Music

JESUS, MELT MY COLD HEART,
Break my stony emotions.
'Cause I've been playing with the waves
When I should be swimming in the ocean.

> *Take me deeper,
> Show me more.
> It's all or nothing;
> I give You everything, my Lord.*

Jesus, show Your mercy,
I'm so sorry for waiting;
I should be running to Your heart,
But I know I've been hesitating.

1393 Martyn Layzell
Copyright © 2001 Thankyou Music

JESUS, MY DESIRE,
I turn towards Your ways.
Hungry for Your truth,
I'm here to seek Your face.

But in my weakness I cry out to You, only
You,
To be my strength when I am weak,
And do as You do.

With You, it all seems so right.
If the sun don't shine,
There's light in Your eyes.
With You, when mountains fall,
I stand on the Rock
And I am safe in Your arms
When I'm with You,
When I'm with You.
(Last time)
Just to be with You.

How can I stay pure?
Oh, how can I stay true?
By living out Your word
And dwelling in Your truth.

1394 Vicky Beeching
Copyright © 2001 Vineyard Songs (UK/Eire)/
Adm. by CopyCare

JESUS, MY PASSION in life is to know You.
May all other goals bow down to
This journey of loving You more.
Jesus, You've showered Your goodness on
me,
Given Your gifts so freely,
But there's one thing I'm longing for.
Hear my heart's cry,
And my prayer for this life.

Above all else, above all else,
Above all else, give me Yourself.

1395 Owen Hurter
Copyright © 2000 Thankyou Music

JESUS, NAME ABOVE ALL NAMES,
My soul cries Jesus,
It's the sweetest song.
Jesus, echoing throughout
All of the heavens,
Angelic hosts proclaim.

Morning Star, Rising Sun,
Lily of the Valley,
Rose of Sharon,
Son of God.
Lifted up, glorified,
Praised through all the ages;
The First and Last,
Beginning and End.

1396 Tim Hughes
Copyright © 2001 Thankyou Music

JESUS, REDEEMER,
Friend and King to me.
My refuge, my comfort,
You're everything to me.
And this heart is on fire for You,
Yes, this heart is on fire for You.

For You alone are wonderful,
You alone are Counsellor,
Everlasting Father,
Mighty in the heavens.
Never to forget the love
You displayed upon a cross,
Son of God, I thank You,
Prince of Peace, I love Your name.

Saviour, Healer,
Just and true are You.
Now reigning in glory,
Most high and living God.
And this heart is in awe of You,
Yes, this heart is in awe of You.

1397 James Gregory
Copyright © 2000 Thankyou Music

JESUS TAUGHT US HOW TO PRAY:
Father, hallowed be Your name.
Would You give us what we need,
And forgive our foolish ways?

I know Jesus only prayed,
Father, what You had ordained.

Let Your kingdom come on earth, Lord, as we
pray.
Let Your will be done to glorify Your name.
Let the kingdom that we live for
Be revealed in us today.
Can I see heaven, can I see heaven
Here on earth today?

1398 Tim Hughes
Copyright © 1999 Thankyou Music

JESUS, YOU ALONE shall be
My first love, my first love.
The secret place and highest praise
Shall be Yours, shall be Yours.

To Your throne I'll bring devotion,
May it be the sweetest sound:
Lord, this heart is reaching for You now.

> *So I'll set my sights upon You,*
> *Set my life upon Your praise;*
> *Never looking to another way.*
> (Second time)
> *You alone will be my passion,*
> *Jesus, You will be my song:*
> *You will find me longing after You.*

Day and night I lift my eyes
To seek You, to seek You,
Hungry for a glimpse of You
In glory, in glory.

1399 Nathan Fellingham
Copyright © 1999 Thankyou Music

JESUS, YOU ARE SO PRECIOUS to me;
To behold You is all I desire.
Seated in glory, now and forever,
My Jesus, my Saviour, my Lord.

> *I worship You,*
> *I worship You,*
> *Lord, I worship You,*
> *Yes, I worship You.*

Jesus, You are so precious to me;
Your beauty has captured my gaze.
Now I will come and bow down before You,
And pour sweet perfume on Your feet.

1400 Sue Rinaldi & Caroline Bonnett
Copyright © 1998 Thankyou Music

JESUS, YOUR BEAUTY is filling this temple.
Jesus, Your fragrance is drawing me closer,
And with every step I take
You lead me into this holy place,
And it washes me clean,
For my eyes have seen
Messiah.

> *And I will jump into the holy river,*
> *I will lose myself to my Deliverer.*
> *I will jump into the holy river,*
> *I will lose myself to my Deliverer.*
> *In this holy place I can see Your face,*
> *Messiah.*

Jesus, Your passion is filling this temple.
Jesus, Your mercy is drawing me closer,
And with every step I take
You lead me into a world that aches,
And I cannot rest till all eyes have seen
Messiah.

1401 Darlene Zschech
Copyright © 1997 Darlene Zschech/
Hillsong Publishing/Kingsway Music

JESUS, YOU'RE ALL I NEED,
You're all I need.
Now I give my life to You alone,
You are all I need.
Jesus, You're all I need,
You're all I need.
Lord, You gave Yourself so I could live,
You are all I need.

Oh, You purchased my salvation,
And wiped away my tears;
Now I drink Your living water,
And I'll never thirst again.
For You alone are holy,
I'll worship at Your throne;
And You will reign forever,
Holy is the Lord.

1402 Martyn Layzell
Copyright © 2000 Thankyou Music

KING JESUS, I BELIEVE
The words of life You breathe,
Your spoken promises,
A guiding light for our feet.
We fall down to our knees
And weep with those who weep:
Let justice flow upon this earth,
A never failing stream.

> *I'm thirsty, longing just to see Your*
> * kingdom come,*
> *Praying that today Your love is shown.*
> *I'm hungry for the will of God to be made*
> * known,*
> *Praying for the day of Your return.*

You have anointed us
To bind the broken heart:
Proclaim deliverance
For those enslaved in the dark.
You pour the oil of joy
All over my despair.
O Spirit of the Sovereign Lord,
Empower us once again.

We pray, we pray,
We pray for the kingdom.
We pray, we pray.
(Repeat)

1403 David Gate
Copyright © 2001 Thankyou Music

KING OF HISTORY, God of eternity,
You beckon me into Your arms,
Where You reveal Your forgiving love
That You lavish on my broken heart.

Such amazing grace that You pour on me,
And You freely give every day I live.
And I'll never know the depth of love
That You gave to me upon the cross.

So I thank You for Your saving love,
So I thank You for Your saving love.

1404 Jarrod Cooper
Copyright © 1996 Sovereign Lifestyle Music

KING OF KINGS, MAJESTY,
God of heaven living in me.
Gentle Saviour, closest Friend,
Strong Deliverer, Beginning and End:
All within me falls at Your throne.

Your majesty, I can but bow;
I lay my all before You now.
In royal robes I don't deserve,
I live to serve Your majesty.

Earth and heaven worship You,
Love eternal, faithful and true,
Who bought the nations, ransomed souls,
Brought this sinner near to Your throne:
All within me cries out in praise.

1405 Doug Horley
Copyright © 1999 Thankyou Music

KING OF LOVE, praise You,
King of love, worship You,
King of love, thank You,
I'm treasure in Your eyes.

I know my heart will love You forever,
I know Your word, I'll always be Your child.
I know my soul is safe for eternity
'Cause You hold me close in Your arms.

Gonna give You all the praise I can,
Gonna give You all the thanks I can.
In Your arms I will be, King of love, holding
  me.
Gonna give You all the love I can,
Gonna give You all the praise I can.
King of love, King of love, I worship You.

1406 David Lyle Morris & Nick Wynne-Jones
Copyright © 2001 Thankyou Music

KING OF OUR LIVES, Your favour rests
On all who know their need of God,
And You will comfort those who mourn.
The humble meek possess the earth,
Your mighty word turns upside down
All that this world considers great.

Jesus, King of our lives, as once they came
To hear Your life-sustaining words,
We gather now with hungry hearts
Your living truth alone can fill.

King of our lives, the pure in heart
Will know the joy of seeing God,
So purify us deep within:
Our thoughts, our words, the things we do,
Your searching word turns inside out –
So touch our hearts and make us clean.

Jesus, we come, sit at Your feet,
Yield You our lives that we may be
Salt of the earth, light of the world.
All of our cares we give to You,
All that we need our Father gives,
So we will put Your kingdom first.

(Final chorus)
King of our lives, as once they came
To hear Your life-transforming word,
We ask You now to rule our hearts
With living words, to do Your will.

King of our lives, Teacher.
Rule in our hearts, Saviour.
King of our lives, Messiah.
Rule in our hearts, Master,
Healer and Friend.

1407 Stuart Townend & Keith Getty
Copyright © 2002 Thankyou Music

KING OF THE AGES, Almighty God,
Perfect love, ever just and true.
Who will not fear You and bring You praise?
All the nations will come to You.

Your ways of love have won my heart,
And brought me joy unending.
Your saving power at work in me,
Bringing peace and the hope of glory.

Your arms of love are reaching out
To every soul that seeks You.
Your light will shine in all the earth,
Bringing grace and a great salvation.

The day will come when You appear,
And every eye shall see You.
Then we shall rise with hearts ablaze,
With a song we will sing forever.

1408 Terry Virgo & Stuart Townend
Copyright © 2001 Thankyou Music

KNOWING YOUR GRACE
Has set me free, Lord.
I'm seeking Your face;
I feel Your pleasure,
Your joy in the ones
You have chosen by name.
You've lifted my burdens
And cast off my shame.

Feeling Your touch
Gives me such peace, Lord.
I love You so much,
I know You'll lead me.
Wherever I go I'll be under Your wing,
For I am a child of the King.

You will finish the work You've begun in me,
I'm adopted, a son in Your family!
You've drawn me with kindness and love
Into this holy place.

What can I say?
Your lavish mercy
Turned night into day –
My guilt has gone now.
Forever I'll stand in Your presence and sing,
For I am a child of the King.

1409 Taizé, music: Jacques Berthier (1923–94)
Copyright © Ateliers et Presses de Taizé

KYRIE, KYRIE ELEISON.
Kyrie, Kyrie eleison.

Lord, Lord, have compassion.
Lord, Lord, have compassion.

1410 Darlene Zschech
Copyright © 1999 Darlene Zschech/
Hillsong Publishing/Kingsway Music

LAMP UNTO MY FEET,
Light unto my path,
It is You, Jesus, it is You.
This treasure that I hold,
More than finest gold,
It is You, Jesus, it is You.

With all my heart, with all my soul,
I live to worship You
And praise forevermore,
Praise forevermore.
Lord, every day I need You more,
On wings of heaven I will soar
With You.

You take my brokenness,
Call me to Yourself.
There You stand,
Healing in Your hands.

1411 David Fellingham
Copyright © 2000 Thankyou Music

LAYING ASIDE EVERYTHING
That would hinder us from coming
Into the presence of our
Great and awesome King;
Lifting up holy hands in faith,
We long to see You face to face,
Freely we come, freely we come.

And we're looking to Jesus,
The One who has saved us.
We're looking to Jesus,
The One who can heal us.
To the Author and the Finisher
Of all that we believe,
Freely we come,
Freely we come.

1412 James Edmeston (1791–1867)
In this version Copyright © Jubilate Hymns Ltd

LEAD US, HEAVENLY FATHER, lead us
Through this world's tempestuous sea;
Guard us, guide us, keep us, feed us –
You our only help and plea;
Here possessing every blessing
If our God our Father be.

Saviour, by Your grace restore us,
All our weaknesses are plain;
You have lived on earth before us,
You have felt our grief and pain:
Tempted, taunted, yet undaunted,
From the depths You rose again.

Spirit of our God, descending,
Fill our hearts with holy peace;
Love with every passion blending,
Pleasure that can never cease:
Thus provided, pardoned, guided,
Ever shall our joys increase.

1413 Liturgy of St James, c.4th cent.
Tr. Gerard Moultrie (1829–85)

LET ALL MORTAL FLESH keep silence
And with fear and trembling stand;
Ponder nothing earthly minded,
For with blessing in His hand
Christ our God to earth descendeth,
Our full homage to demand.

King of kings, yet born of Mary,
As of old on earth He stood,
Lord of lords, in human vesture,
In the body and the blood:
He will give to all the faithful
His own self for heavenly food.

Rank on rank the host of heaven
Spreads its vanguard on the way,
As the Light of light descendeth
From the realms of endless day,
That the powers of hell may vanish
As the darkness clears away.

At His feet the six-winged seraph;
Cherubim with sleepless eye,
Veil their faces to the Presence,
As with ceaseless voice they cry,
Alleluia, alleluia,
Alleluia, Lord most high!

1414 Darrell Patton Evans
Copyright © 1995 Mercy/Vineyard Publishing/
Adm. by CopyCare

LET THE POOR MAN SAY, I AM RICH IN HIM;
Let the lost man say I am found in Him:
Let the river flow.
Let the blind man say, I can see again;
Let that dead man say, I am born again:
Let the river flow.

Let the river flow,
Let the river flow,
Let the river flow.
Holy Spirit, come;
Move in power.
Let the river flow.
(Let the river flow)

1415 Bruce Napier
Copyright © 1998 Bruce Napier

LET THERE BE JOY, let there be peace,
Let there be power, let there be praise.
Let there be joy, joy in the Holy Ghost.
It was for freedom that we were set free,
Let every mountain be cast to the sea.
Let there be joy, joy in the Holy Ghost.

We will declare it to the heavens,
The righteousness of God in which we stand.
We will proclaim it to the nations;
Every eye shall see, every ear shall hear,
Every heart will understand.

1416 Reuben Morgan
Copyright © 1998 Reuben Morgan/
Hillsong Publishing/Kingsway Music

LET THE WEAK SAY I AM STRONG,
Let the poor say I am rich,
Let the blind say I can see,
It's what the Lord has done in me.
(Repeat)

> *Hosanna, hosanna*
> *To the Lamb that was slain;*
> *Hosanna, hosanna,*
> *Jesus died and rose again.*

Into the river I will wade,
There my sins are washed away;
From the heavens mercy streams
Of the Saviour's love for me.

I will rise from waters deep
Into the saving arms of God;
I will sing salvation songs:
Jesus Christ has set me free.

1417 David Lyle Morris
Copyright © 2000 Thankyou Music

LET US RUN WITH PERSEVERANCE
The race set out before us;
Let us fix our eyes on Jesus,
The Author and Perfecter of our faith.

In the beginning
The Word was with God,
Through Him all of us were made;
He began a work in us,
A good work to perfect
Until He returns again.

Since we are surrounded
By heaven's cheering crowd,
Let us throw off every chain:
For all that opposes us,
Look to Jesus who endured
So we'll not lose heart again.

For the joy before Him,
He suffered the cross,
He defeated death and shame;
Now He reigns in glory
At the right hand of God –
He is calling us by name.

1418
G.W. Kitchin (1827–1912)
& M.R. Newbolt (1874–1956)
Copyright © Hymns Ancient & Modern Ltd

LIFT HIGH THE CROSS, *the love of Christ
proclaim
Till all the world adore His sacred name!*

Come, brethren, follow where our Captain
trod,
Our King victorious, Christ the Son of God.

Each new-born soldier of the Crucified
Bears on his brow the seal of Him who died.

This is the sign which Satan's legions fear
And angels veil their faces to revere.

Saved by this cross whereon their Lord was
slain,
The sons of Adam their lost home regain.

From north and south, from east and west
they raise
In growing unison their song of praise.

O Lord, once lifted on the glorious tree,
As Thou hast promised, draw men unto
Thee.

Let every race and every language tell
Of Him who saves our souls from death and
hell.

Set up Thy throne, that earth's despair may
cease
Beneath the shadow of its healing peace.

1419
Tim Hughes
Copyright © 2000 Thankyou Music

LIGHT OF THE WORLD,
You stepped down into darkness,
Opened my eyes, let me see
Beauty that made this heart adore You,
Hope of a life spent with You.

*So here I am to worship,
Here I am to bow down,
Here I am to say that You're my God;
And You're altogether lovely,
Altogether worthy,
Altogether wonderful to me.*

King of all days,
Oh so highly exalted,
Glorious in heaven above;
Humbly You came
To the earth You created,
All for love's sake became poor.

And I'll never know how much it cost
To see my sin upon that cross.
(Repeat)

1420
Paul Oakley
Copyright © 2001 Thankyou Music

LIKE A FRAGRANT OIL,
Like costly perfume poured out,
Let my worship be to You.
Like a fervent prayer,
Like incense rising to Your throne,
In spirit and in truth.

*Jesus,
You alone are worthy of my praise,
I owe my life to You.
Jesus,
You alone can make me holy,
So I bow before You.*

Like a wedding vow,
'All I am I give to You',
Let my sacrifice be pure.
Like the sweetest sound,
Like a lover's whisper in Your ear,
I've set my heart on You.

1421
Stuart Townend
Copyright © 1999 Thankyou Music

LIKE THE SUNSHINE after rainfall,
Like the gentle breeze;
Like the stillness of the morning,
Like the radiant trees:
These things I knew before,
But never have they spoken such life to me;
Oh, the wonder of a Maker
Whose heart delights in me.

Like the nurture of a baby
At its mother's breast;
Like the closeness of a lover,
Like two souls at rest:
These things I knew before,
But never have they spoken such peace to
me;
Oh, the wonder of Maker
Whose heart delights in me.

The heavens declare His magnificence,
The earth resounds with His praise;
Be still my soul, and be satisfied
To worship Him,
To worship Him.

Like the vastness of a desert,
Like the ocean's roar;
Like the greatness of the mountains,
Where the eagles soar:
These things I knew before,
But never have they spoken such power to
   me;
Oh, the wonder of a Maker
Whose heart delights in me.

1422 Graham Kendrick
Copyright © 1984 Thankyou Music

LOOK TO THE SKIES, there's a celebration,
Lift up your heads, join the angel song,
For our Creator becomes our Saviour,
As a baby born!
Angels, amazed, bow in adoration:
'Glory to God in the highest heaven!'
Send the good news out to every nation
For our hope has come.

> *Worship the King – come, see His*
>   *brightness;*
> *Worship the King, His wonders tell:*
> *Jesus our King is born today;*
> *We welcome You, Emmanuel!*

Wonderful Counsellor, Mighty God,
Father forever, the Prince of Peace:
There'll be no end to Your rule of justice,
For it shall increase.
Light of Your face, come to pierce our
   darkness;
Joy of Your heart come to chase our gloom;
Star of the morning, a new day dawning,
Make our hearts Your home.

Quietly He came as a helpless baby –
One day in power He will come again;
Swift through the skies He will burst with
   splendour
On the earth to reign.
Jesus, I bow at Your manger lowly:
Now in my life let Your will be done;
Live in my flesh by Your Spirit holy
Till Your kingdom comes.

1423 Matt Redman
Copyright © 1998 Thankyou Music

LORD, HEAR THE MUSIC OF MY HEART;
Hear all the pourings of my soul.
Songs telling of a life of love:
Jesus, this is all for You.
You've become the ruler of my heart;
You've become the lover of my soul.
You've become the Saviour of this life:
You are everything to me.

(Oh now,) Jesus, Jesus,
I will pour my praise on You.
Worship, worship,
Demonstrates my love for You.
May I come to
Be a blessing to Your heart.
Jesus, Jesus,
Who can tell how wonderful You are,
How wonderful You are!

O, how wonderful You are.

1424 Matt Redman
Copyright © 1998 Thankyou Music

LORD, I AM NOT MY OWN,
No longer my own,
Living now for You,
And everything I think,
All I say and do
Is for You, my Lord.

Now taking up the cross,
Walking on Your paths,
Holding out Your truth,
Running in this race,
Bowing every day,
All for You, my Lord.

> *And what I have vowed*
> *I will make good.*
> *Every promise made*
> *Will be fulfilled,*
> *Till the day I die,*
> *Every day I live*
> *Is for You, is for You, is for You,*
> *Is for You, is for You, is for You.*

Earth has nothing I desire
That lives outside of You,
I'm consumed with You.
Treasures have no hold,
Nothing else will do,
Only You, my Lord.

1425 Geraldine Latty
Copyright © 2000 Thankyou Music

LORD, I COME, longing to know You,
Lord, I come, drawn by Your love;
Lord, I come, longing to see Your face,
For You called me to come
Into the holiest place.

> *What did I do to deserve Your favour?*
> *What did I do to deserve Your grace?*
> *Called by my name into Your presence,*
> *Undeserved, holy God.*

Lord, I come, because of Jesus,
Lord, I come, because He came;
Lord, I bow, as You reveal Your face,
You have called me to come
Into the holiest place.

1426

Colse Leung
Copyright © 2001 Thankyou Music

LORD, I COME TO YOU,
Broken and lost,
Jesus, be the highest part.
Here I am again,
Longing for more,
Waiting for Your presence, here,
Your presence here.

And how can I do anything but praise You?
How can I not worship You,
And how can I live my life
Without You, God?
Lord, You amaze me with Your favour,
Lord, You astound me with Your love,
And how can I live my life
Without You, God?

1427

Stuart Townend & Fred Heumann
Copyright © 2002 Thankyou Music

LORD, I'M GRATEFUL,
Amazed at what You've done.
My finest efforts are filthy rags;
But I'm made righteous
By trusting in the Son:
I have God's riches at Christ's expense!

'Cause it's grace!
There's nothing I can do
To make You love me more,
To make You love me less than You do.
And by faith
I'm standing on this Stone
Of Christ and Christ alone,
Your righteousness is all that I need,
'Cause it's grace!

Called and chosen when I was far away,
You brought me into Your family.
Free, forgiven, my guilt is washed away;
Your loving kindness is life to me.

Grace loves the sinner,
Loves all I am and all I'll ever be;
Makes me a winner
Whatever lies the devil throws at me.

Freely given, but bought with priceless blood,
My life was ransomed at Calvary.
There my Jesus gave everything He could
That I might live for eternity.

1428

Marilyn Baker
Copyright © 1998 Marilyn Baker Music/
Kingsway Music

LORD, I WANT TO TELL YOU
How much I love You;
Your tenderness and mercy
Have overwhelmed my heart.
Let my whole life be
An overflow of worship:
All I have and all I am
I give back, Lord, to You.

Lord, I want to tell You
My heart's desire,
The love You've put within me
Will burn with holy fire.
Let my actions spring
From an overflow of worship:
All I have and all I am
I gladly give back to You.

1429

Philip Lawson Johnston
Copyright © 1997 Thankyou Music

LORD JESUS, ROBED IN SPLENDOUR,
Clothed in glory high over all.
Lord Jesus, King Messiah,
Mighty Saviour, high over all.

Lord Jesus, all resplendent,
Adorned in beauty, who can compare?
Lord Jesus, You are mighty,
Your kingdom rules high over all.

Yours is the name by which we are saved,
The Name high over all.
Yours is the name which we will proclaim,
For You are Lord of all.
Jesus, Lord, high over,
Jesus, Lord, high over all!

The heavens declare the glory of God;
The skies proclaim the work of His hands.
The earth will be filled
With the knowledge of His glory
As the waters cover the sea.

1430

Matt Redman
Copyright © 1998 Thankyou Music

LORD, LET YOUR GLORY FALL
As on that ancient day;
Songs of enduring love,
And then Your glory came.
And as a sign to You
That we would love the same,
Our hearts will sing that song:
God, let Your glory come.

You are good, You are good,
And Your love endures.
You are good, You are good,
And Your love endures.
You are good, You are good,
And Your love endures today.

Voices in unison,
Giving You thanks and praise,
Joined by the instruments,
And then Your glory came.
Your presence like a cloud
Upon that ancient day;
The priests were overwhelmed
Because Your glory came.

A sacrifice was made,
And then Your fire came;
They knelt upon the ground,
And with one voice they praised.
(Repeat)

1431 Mark Baldry
Copyright © 1999 Thankyou Music

LORD, MY REQUEST,
Lord, my desire
Is to touch Your very heart
Through the way I live my life.
Jesus, all I seek,
Saviour, all I want
Is a passion for Your ways
And a heart that longs for You,
Yes, a heart that longs for You.

It's the way You walk with me,
It's the way You talk with me,
And You sacrificed Your all to give me life.
It's the way You took that cross
With Your arms held out in love,
Yes, You sacrificed Your all to give me life.

You gave Your all to give me life. *(×4)*

1432 Stuart Townend
Copyright © 2001 Thankyou Music

LORD OF EVERY HEART,
I'm coming back to You.
I'm standing in the shallows
Of what Your love can do;
Remembering the joy
Of laughter in the rain,
I'm calling from the desert,
Won't You fill me again?

Fill me again, won't You fill me again?
I'm tired and I'm thirsty
And I've come to the end.
Come cleanse me with fire,
Refresh me with rain.
O Breath of the Spirit, come closer.

Lord of every deed,
Your promise is enough;
You're unreserved in mercy,
And unrestrained in love.
I'm casting down these crowns
Of all that I can do;
I'm trading my ambitions
For a touch of You.

1433 Timothy Dudley-Smith
Copyright © Timothy Dudley-Smith

LORD OF THE CHURCH,
We pray for our renewing:
Christ over all, our undivided aim;
Fire of the Spirit, burn for our enduing,
Wind of the Spirit, fan the living flame!
We turn to Christ amid our fear and failing,
The will that lacks the courage to be free,
The weary labours, all but unavailing,
To bring us nearer what a church should be.

Lord of the church, we seek a Father's
   blessing,
A true repentance and a faith restored,
A swift obedience and a new possessing,
Filled with the Holy Spirit of the Lord!
We turn to Christ from all our restless striving,
Unnumbered voices with a single prayer:
The living water for our souls' reviving,
In Christ to live, and love and serve and care.

Lord of the church, we long for our uniting,
True to one calling, by one vision stirred;
One cross proclaiming and one creed
   reciting,
One in the truth of Jesus and His word!
So lead us on; till toil and trouble ended,
One church triumphant one new song shall
   sing,
To praise His glory, risen and ascended,
Christ over all, the everlasting King!

1434 David Lyle Morris & Nick Wynne-Jones
Copyright © 2001 Thankyou Music

LORD OF THE CHURCH,
You hold us in Your hand,
And know us through and through.
You speak to us
Of love and faith and strength,
And of our weakness too.

From love grown cold,
Faint faith that seems alive,
From lukewarm lives and pride.
We turn to You,
That we may be revived,
On fire with love renewed.

Your Spirit is speaking,
Your church is listening
To hear, and to obey.

From compromise,
With all that is not true,
With all that is not pure,
We turn to You.
That we may be full of faith,
Holy in all we do.

Lord of the Church,
Your Spirit speaks in love,
To call us back to You.
We ask You, Lord,
To share Your life with us,
And fill Your church with power.

Your Spirit is speaking,
Your church is listening;
We'll hear, and we'll obey,
Lord of the Church.

1435 Shaun & Mel Griffiths
Copyright © 1998 Parachute Music New Zealand/
Adm. by Kingsway Music

LORD OF THE HEAVENS,
I bow my knee and worship You;
I stand before You,
And I am amazed.
I see Your beauty
Displayed in everything You do.

For You are my Saviour, Lord and King,
You are the only One for me;
You are the only One that I adore.
In Your Son atonement, sacrifice:
Through His death redemption gives new life,
And I reach out, receive Your endless love.

1436 James & Hayley Gregory
Copyright © 2000 Thankyou Music

LORD, TO LOVE YOU MORE is all I want,
To hear You speaking to my heart,
To be consumed by You again.
Fix my eyes on You and draw me near,
Let all distractions disappear,
I need You even more today.

For Jesus, I am overwhelmed
By all Your love has done,
And all I want to say is that I adore You, Lord.
I'm humbled by the grace of God,
You met my every need,
And Jesus, You will be always my greatest
love.

I adore You. *(x4)*

1437 Martin E. Leckebusch
Copyright © 1999 Kevin Mayhew Ltd

LORD, WE THANK YOU FOR THE PROMISE
Seen in every human birth;
You have planned each new beginning:
Who could hope for greater worth?
Hear our prayer for those we cherish,
Claim our children as Your own:
In the fertile ground of childhood
May eternal seed be sown.

Lord, we thank You for the vigour
Burning in the years of youth:
Strength to face tomorrow's challenge,
Zest for life and zeal for truth.
In the choice of friends and partners,
When ideas and values form,
May the message of Your kingdom
Be the guide, the goal, the norm.

Lord, we thank You for the harvest
Of the settled, middle years:
Times when work and home can prosper,
When life's richest fruit appears;
But when illness, stress and hardship
Fill so many days with dread,
May Your love renew the vision
Of a clearer road ahead.

Lord, we thank You for the beauty
Of a heart at last mature:
Crowned with peace and rich in wisdom,
Well-respected and secure;
But to those who face the twilight
Frail, bewildered, lacking friends,
Lord, confirm Your gracious offer:
Perfect life which never ends.

1438 Ken Riley
Copyright © 2001 Thankyou Music

LORD, WHEN I THINK OF YOU,
And what I put You through,
I'll never understand Your endless mercy.
To think You chose to come,
Embodied in Your Son
To fall into the hands of Your created.
Oh, feel my heart explode with praise, yeah.

I give You all my love, I give You
  everything.
You are God of heaven, and head over
  heels with me!
I know You burn with passion, when I call
  on Your name,
Your love runs as a river, washing my
  shame away,
Restoring my faith again, yeah.

How did You look upon
The sight of Your own blood?
You even took the sin of those who nailed
  You!
For grace and justice meet
In Him who's chosen me
To walk a path that takes me on to heaven.
Oh, feel my heart explode with praise, yeah.

1439   Andrew Rogers
          Copyright © 2001 Thankyou Music

LORD, YOU ARE MY RIGHTEOUSNESS,
The One who sanctifies my life,
My Shepherd and my guide.
Banner of deliverance,
Warrior and my defence,
In Your secret place I hide.
Every other throne must fall
And proclaim You Lord of all
At the mention of Your name;
My salvation and my light,
In Your presence I abide
And Your righteousness I claim.

  Jesus, Jesus,
  Jesus, Jesus.

Though You are the King of kings,
Yet You are my next of kin,
And my nearest friend.
Laying down Your life for me,
Your amazing grace I see,
And Your love without an end.
How can I keep silent, Lord?
Even stones obey Your word
And they give to You their praise.
You're the Lord of everything,
All creation's voices sing
Of the glory of Your name.

1440   John Hartley & Gary Sadler
          Copyright © 2000 worshiptogether.com songs/
          Adm. by Kingsway Music/& Integrity's Hosanna!
          Music/Sovereign Music UK

LORD, YOU SEE ME through Your mercy:
I am guilty, still You love me.
In Your kindness there is justice;
Through Your goodness,
You have brought me

Here, where truth and mercy meet,
You triumph over me,
Your love has won my heart again.
And still I am so amazed,
My guilt is washed away
Before Your cross of peace,
Where truth and mercy meet.

King of glory, Lord of mercy,
Risen Saviour, Perfect Wonder.
Through Your kindness
You have drawn me,
By Your suffering
You have saved me.

1441   Graham Kendrick
          Copyright © 2001 Make Way Music

LORD, YOU'VE BEEN GOOD TO ME
All my life, all my life;
Your loving kindness never fails.
I will remember all You have done,
Bring from my heart thanksgiving songs.

  New every morning is Your love,
  Filled with compassion from above.
  Grace and forgiveness full and free,
  Lord, You've been good to me.

So, may each breath I take
Be for You, Lord, only You,
Giving You back the life I owe.
Love so amazing, mercy so free.
Lord, You've been good,
So good to me.

1442   Stuart Townend
          Copyright © 2000 Thankyou Music

LOVE IS PATIENT, love is kind,
It does not envy or speak in pride.
It does not seek its own reward:
Oh, that's how You love me, Lord.

It always hopes and perseveres,
It covers over a wealth of sins,
It shuns all evil, delights in truth:
Oh, I want to be like You.

  I'm in love with a King,
  I'm in love with a Friend,
  And whatever I do
  This love never ends.
  He's for me, He pleads for me,
  Pours out His life for me;
  What more do I need?
  Amazing love!

There are tongues now, but they will cease;
There is knowledge – it's incomplete.
For what we know now, we know in part,
But what endures is a loving heart.

1443 David Lyle Morris
Copyright © 2000 Thankyou Music

LOVE, JOY, PEACE *and patience,*
Kindness, goodness, faithfulness,
Gentleness and self-control:
This is the fruit of the Spirit.
We want the fruit of the Spirit.
Love, joy, peace and patience,
Kindness, goodness, faithfulness,
Gentleness and self-control:
We will reap what we sow,
We will reap what we sow.

We want joy in the Spirit,
We will rejoice in the Spirit of God.
There is peace in the Spirit,
We want to rest in the Spirit of God.

We want life in the Spirit,
We want to live by the Spirit of God.
Keep in step with the Spirit,
We will be led by the Spirit of God.

Walking with the Spirit of Jesus.
Living by the Spirit of Jesus.
Rejoicing in the Spirit of Jesus.
Resting in the Spirit of Jesus.

1444 Steve Bassett & Sue Rinaldi
Copyright © 2002 Thankyou Music

LOVE LIKE A JEWEL has come down,
Most precious gem
In heaven's crown.
Love like a jewel has come down,
The greatest treasure
That I have found.

And I will seek after You,
Forsake everything that is distracting me
From this searching,
And run to the place
Where my heart only hears the beat
Of Your love for this world.

Love like a jewel has come down,
You walk with the hurting,
You're a friend to the poor.
Love like a jewel has come down,
Our greatest treasure,
Where hope can be found.

1445 Taizé, music: Jacques Berthier (1923–94)
Copyright © Ateliers et Presses de Taizé

MAGNIFICAT, magnificat,
Magnificat anima mea Dominum.
Magnificat, magnificat,
Magnificat anima mea!

Sing out, my soul; sing out, my soul.
Sing out and glorify the Lord who sets us
free.
Sing out, my soul; sing out, my soul.
Sing out and glorify the Lord God!

1446 Matt Redman
Copyright © 1997 Thankyou Music

MANY ARE THE WORDS WE SPEAK,
Many are the songs we sing;
Many kinds of offerings,
But now to live the life.
(Repeat)

Help us live the life,
Help us live the life.
All we want to do
Is bring You something real,
Bring You something true.

(We hope that)
Precious are the words we speak,
(We pray that)
Precious are the songs we sing;
Precious all these offerings,
But now to live the life.

Now to go the extra mile,
Now to turn the other cheek,
And to serve You with a life.
Let us share Your fellowship,
Even of Your sufferings;
Never let the passion die.

Now to live the life. (×6)

1447 Doug Horley
Copyright © 1999 Thankyou Music

MAY MY EYES SEE MORE OF YOU, Lord;
May my heart just beat with Yours.
May my hope be in Your goodness,
May my life be pure.
And every day my cry is just the same:
Make me like Jesus, Lord, I pray.

Because You've captured my heart,
You have captured my heart.
King of love, and King of glory,
Author of creation's story,
I delight in You, and now and forever.
You have captured my heart,
You have captured my heart.
I delight in You, You've captured my heart.

Because You've captured my heart,
You have captured my heart.
In Your throne room there will be
No hiding place in purity,
A life laid bare for all to see,
O God, make me holy.
You have captured my heart,
You have captured my heart.
I delight in You, You've captured my heart.

1448

Kate B. Wilkinson (1859–1928)

MAY THE MIND OF CHRIST MY SAVIOUR
Live in me from day to day,
By His love and power controlling
All I do and say.

May the word of God dwell richly
In my heart from hour to hour,
So that all may see I triumph
Only through His power.

May the peace of God my Father
Rule my life in everything,
That I may be calm to comfort
Sick and sorrowing.

May the love of Jesus fill me,
As the waters fill the sea;
Him exalting, self abasing,
This is victory.

May I run the race before me,
Strong and brave to face the foe,
Looking only unto Jesus,
As I onward go.

1449

Tim Hughes & Rob Hill
Copyright © 2000 Thankyou Music

MAY THE WORDS OF MY MOUTH,
And the thoughts of my heart
Bless Your name, bless Your name, Jesus:
And the deeds of the day,
And the truth in my ways,
Speak of You, speak of You, Jesus.

For this is what I'm glad to do,
It's time to live a life of love
That pleases You.
And I will give my all to You,
Surrender everything I have and follow
You,
I'll follow You.

Lord, will You be my vision,
Lord, will You be my guide:
Be my hope, be my light, and the way?
And I'll look not for riches,
Nor praises on earth,
Only You'll be the first of my heart.

I will follow, I will follow You. *(×4)*

1450

S. Monteiro, English: Word & Music
Copyright © S. Monteiro / Copyright Control
English words © 1995 Word & Music/
Jubilate Hymns Ltd

MERCIFUL LORD, in Your lovingkindness
Hear our prayer, listen to our intercession.
Merciful Lord, in Your lovingkindness
Hear our prayer, listen to our intercession.

Ouve Senhor, eu estou clamando,
Tem piedade de mim e me responde.
Ouve Senhor, eu estou clamando,
Tem piedade de mim e me responde.

1451

Lynn DeShazo & Gary Sadler
Copyright © 1997 Integrity's Hosanna! Music/
Sovereign Music UK

MERCY, *mercy, Lord,*
Your mercy is how we are restored;
Mercy, O mercy, Lord,
Help us to show Your mercy, Lord.

You have been patient with our offences,
You have forgiven all of our sins;
We were deserving only Your judgement,
But Your great mercy triumphed again.

Lord, You have taught us, 'Love one another,'
As You have loved us so we must love;
Always forbearing, always forgiving,
Showing to others the mercy we've known.

1452 Reuben Morgan
Copyright © 1999 Reuben Morgan/
Hillsong Publishing/Kingsway Music

MORE THAN I COULD HOPE OR DREAM OF,
You have poured Your favour on me.
One day in the house of God is
Better than a thousand days in the world.
So blessed, I can't contain it,
So much I've got to give it away.
Your love has taught me to live, now,
You are more than enough for me.

1453 James Taylor
Copyright © 1997 Thankyou Music

MY FRIEND AND KING,
Love sweeter than a rose;
You meet me where I am.
What can I do
But bow down on my knees?
Your beauty blows my mind.

Lord, I will call only to You,
For You deserve the highest praise.
And I will live only for You,
For You deserve the highest praise.

To be with You
Is all that I desire;
Lord, may You shine in me.
You gave me life
And sacrificed Your own;
Who else would die for me?

1454 Kate Simmonds & Mark Edwards
Copyright © 2002 Thankyou Music

MY GOD IS A ROCK! My feet are planted
And I'm not gonna stop praising.
This love is alive!
Goodness and mercy all the days of my life.

My God is a Rock who can't be shaken,
No, I won't ever stop praising.
This love is alive
With every promise written over my life.

And in Him I live, for He lives in me.
And in Him I move, and I have my being.
I'm held forever in Your hand
(Rock solid, rock solid).
And now this ground on which I stand
(Is rock solid, it's rock solid).

My God is a Rock and my salvation,
That's why I'll never stop praising.
This love is alive!
My strength and shelter all the days of my
   life.

My God is a Rock who never changes,
How can I ever stop praising?
This love is alive!
Night and day He's watching over my life.

1455 Author unknown
Copyright control

MY GOD IS SO BIG, so strong and so mighty,
There's nothing that He cannot do.
My God is so big, so strong and so mighty,
There's nothing that He cannot do.
The rivers are His, the mountains are His,
The stars are His handiwork too.
My God is so big, so strong and so mighty,
There's nothing that He cannot do.

My God is so big, so strong and so mighty,
There's nothing that He cannot do.
My God is so big, so strong and so mighty,
There's nothing that He cannot do.
He's called you to live for Him every day,
In all that you say and you do.
My God is so big, so strong and so mighty,
There's nothing that He cannot do.

1456 Lara Martin (Abundant Life Ministries,
Bradford, England)
Copyright © 2002 Thankyou Music

MY HEART IS CAPTIVATED, LORD, by You
   alone;
Captured by the awesomeness of You alone.
Melted by the grace and mercy You have
   shown,
I stand in wonder.
I reach to You,
The One who makes the blind eyes see,
Who breaks the chains of sickness with authority.
Restoring what was broken,
So it may fly again.

I live to worship You;
I breathe to worship You.
All of my days Your face I will seek.
For as I worship You,
You lead me to that place,
To that place of divine exchange.

1457 Robin Mark
Copyright © 2000 Thankyou Music

MY HOPE IS IN THE LORD
Who has renewed my strength,
When everything seems senseless,
My hope is still in Him
Who has made heaven and earth
And things seen and unseen;
Whatever shade of passing day,
My hope is still in Him.

My hope is in You, Lord.
My hope is in You, Lord.
My hope is in You, Lord.
My hope is in You, Lord.

For I know that my eyes shall see You,
In the latter days to come.
When You stand on the earth,
With my lips, I will confess
That the hope of my heart is come,
That the hope of my heart is come.

1458 Keith Getty & Richard Creighton
Copyright © 2001 Thankyou Music

MY HOPE RESTS FIRM on Jesus Christ,
He is my only plea:
Though all the world should point and scorn,
His ransom leaves me free,
His ransom leaves me free.

My hope sustains me as I strive
And strain towards the goal;
Though I still stumble into sin,
His death paid for it all,
His death paid for it all.

My hope provides me with a spur
To help me run this race:
I know my tears will turn to joy
The day I see His face,
The day I see His face.

My hope is to be with my Lord,
To know as I am known:
To serve Him gladly all my days
In praise before His throne,
In praise before His throne.

1459 Robert Critchley
Copyright © 2001 Thankyou Music

MY TROUBLED SOUL, why so weighed
down?
You were not made to bear this heavy load.
Cast all Your burdens upon the Lord;
Jesus cares, He cares for you.

Jesus cares, He cares for you.
And all your worrying
Won't help you make it through.
Cast all your burdens upon the Lord.
And trust again in the promise of His love.

I will praise the mighty name of Jesus,
Praise the Lord, the lifter of my head.
Praise the Rock of my salvation,
All my days are in His faithful hands.

My anxious heart, why so upset?
When trials come, how you so easily forget
To cast your burdens upon the Lord;
Jesus cares, He cares for you.

1460 Neil Bennetts
Copyright © 2000 Daybreak Music Ltd

NAME ABOVE ALL NAMES,
The Saviour for sinners slain.
You suffered for my sake
To bring me back home again.
When I was lost,
You poured Your life out for me.
Name above all names,
Jesus, I love You.

Giver of mercy,
The fountain of life for me.
My spirit is lifted
To soar on the eagle's wings.
What love is this
That fills my heart with treasure?
Name above all names,
Jesus, I love You.

High King eternal,
The one true and faithful God.
The beautiful Saviour,
Still reigning in power and love.
With all my heart
I'll worship You forever:
Name above all names,
Jesus, I love You.

1461 Matt Redman
Copyright © 1993 Thankyou Music

NO LONGER JUST SERVANTS in the house
of the King,
The banquet is ready and You draw us in.
You call us to eat with You and to be
Your friends, those who love You,
Your friends, those who know You.

Oh, how can it be that I have become
A friend of the King after all that I've done?
A sinner in rags, now a child in Your care,
You showed me the cross and I met You
there.
Your friend, one who loves You,
Your friend, one who knows You.

A servant is trusted with some secret things,
And so, how much more for the friend of a
King.
No eye has yet seen, and no ear has heard
What You've prepared for those who love You
What You've prepared for those who love You.

And I'll sing a song for the One that I love,
You captured my heart when I met with Your
Son.
And so I will live a life full of praise
For You, Lord and Shepherd,
For You, Friend and King.

1462 Geraldine Latty
Copyright © 2002 Thankyou Music

NONE OTHER is more worthy,
None other is more deserving of our praise.
None other is so holy,
Sovereign God we come to You,
We give the glory due Your name.

1463 Graham Kendrick
Copyright © 1997 Make Way Music

NO SCENES OF STATELY MAJESTY for the
King of kings.
No nights aglow with candle flame for the
King of love.
No flags of empire hung in shame for
Calvary.
No flowers perfumed the lonely way that led
Him to
A borrowed tomb for Easter Day.

No wreaths upon the ground were laid for
the King of kings.
Only a crown of thorns remained where He
gave His love.
A message scrawled in irony – 'King of the
Jews' –
Lay trampled where they turned away, and
no one knew
That it was the first Easter Day.

Yet nature's finest colours blaze for the King
of kings.
And stars in jewelled clusters say, 'Worship
heaven's King.'
Two thousand springtimes more have
bloomed – is that enough?
Oh, how can I be satisfied until He hears
The whole world sing of Easter love?

My prayers shall be a fragrance sweet for the
King of kings.
My love the flowers at His feet for the King of
love.
My vigil is to watch and pray until He comes;
My highest tribute to obey and live to know
The power of that first Easter Day.

I long for scenes of majesty for the risen
King.
Or nights aglow with candle flame for the
King of love.
A nation hushed upon its knees at Calvary,
Where all our sins and griefs were nailed
And hope was born of everlasting Easter Day.

1464 Martyn Layzell
Copyright © 1999 Thankyou Music

NOT BY WORDS AND NOT BY DEEDS,
But by grace we have been saved;
And it is the gift of God, the faith we need.
Not by strength and not by might,
But with power from on high,
So that we can only boast, boast in You.

For once I was dead, now I'm alive,
For freedom I'm set free;
And in Your great love, life do I find.
You opened up my eyes.

Not with eloquence or fame,
But in weakness and in shame,
For the power of Your strength is then
revealed.
And the message of Your cross,
Seemed such foolishness to some,
But the mercy of Your grace is hidden there.

1465 Tim Hughes
Copyright © 1998 Thankyou Music

NOTHING IN THIS WORLD,
No treasure man could buy,
Could take the place of drawing near to You.
There's nothing I want more
Than to spend my days with You,
Dwelling in Your secret place of praise.

And oh, how I need You.
Jesus, I need You.
You are the One that satisfies,
You are the One that satisfies.

So place within my heart
A fire that burns for You,
That waters cannot quench
Nor wash away.
And let that fire blaze
Through all eternity,
Where one day I shall see You face to face.

1466 Matt Redman & Mike Pilavachi
Copyright © 2000 Thankyou Music

NOTHING IS TOO MUCH TO ASK
Now that I have said I'm Yours,
Jesus, take the whole of me
Unreservedly.

Jesus, take me deeper now
That I might go further too,
I've received so much from You
Undeservedly.

I was made to love You, Lord,
I was saved to worship You.
You will be the focus
Of all eternity.

1467 Mark Stevens (Abundant Life Ministries,
Bradford, England)
Copyright © 2002 Thankyou Music

NOW HAS COME SALVATION,
Now has come Your strength,
And the kingdom of my God,
And the power of His Christ,
Jesus, holy One,
Jesus, holy One.

You are the One that I love, my Lord,
You are the One all of heaven adores.
You are the One who is high
Over all the earth.
Jesus, my risen Saviour,
Jesus, my risen Saviour.

Now has come Your mercy,
Now has come Your peace,
And the glory of Your presence,
And the greatness of Your name,
Jesus, holy One,
Jesus, holy One.

Now has come forgiveness,
Now has come Your grace,
And the precious Holy Spirit,
And the freedom that You gave
In Jesus, holy One,
Jesus, holy One.

1468 Graham Kendrick
Copyright © 1993 Make Way Music

NOW, IN REVERENCE AND AWE
We gather round Your word;
In wonder we draw near
To mysteries that angels strain to hear,
That prophets dimly saw:
So let Your Spirit
Shine upon the page and...

Teach me,
Open my eyes with truth to free me,
Light to chase the lies.
Lord Jesus, let me meet You in Your word;
Lord Jesus, let me meet You in Your word.

Lord, Your truth cannot be chained,
It searches everything –
My secrets, my desires.
Your word is like a hammer and a fire,
It breaks, it purifies:
So let Your Spirit
Shine into my heart and...

1469 Timothy Dudley-Smith
Copyright © Timothy Dudley-Smith

O CHANGELESS CHRIST, forever new,
Who walked our earthly ways,
Still draw our hearts as once You drew
The hearts of other days.

As once You spoke by plain and hill
Or taught by shore and sea,
So be today our teacher still,
O Christ of Galilee.

As wind and storm their Master heard
And His command fulfilled,
May troubled hearts receive Your word,
The tempest-tossed be stilled.

And as of old to all who prayed
Your healing hand was shown,
So be Your touch upon us laid,
Unseen but not unknown.

In broken bread, in wine outpoured,
Your new and living way
Proclaim to us, O risen Lord,
O Christ of this our day.

O changeless Christ, till life is past
Your blessing still be given;
Then bring us home, to taste at last
The timeless joys of heaven.

1470 Marty Sampson
Copyright © 1999 Marty Sampson/
Hillsong Publishing/Kingsway Music

O DEAR GOD, WE ASK FOR YOUR FAVOUR,
Come and sweep through this place.
Oh, we desire You.
I just want to be with You, be where You are,
Dwell in Your presence, O God.
Oh, I want to walk with You.

And I will climb this mountain,
And I step off the shore;
And I have chosen to follow,
And be by Your side forevermore.

Tell me what You want me to do, Lord God,
Tell me what You want for my life.
It's Yours, O God, it's Yours.
Do Your will, have Your way,
Be Lord God in this place.
Oh, I want Your will to be done.

1471 William Cowper (1731–1800), adapt. Keith Getty
Copyright © 2001 Thankyou Music

O FOR A CLOSER WALK WITH GOD,
A calm and heavenly frame.
A light that shines upon the road,
Leading to the Lamb.

Where is the blessèdness I knew
When I once saw the Lord?
Where is the soul refreshing view
Living in His word?

A light to be my guide,
The Father's presence at my side.
In Your will my rest I find.
O for a closer walk with God,
Leading to the Lamb.

So shall my walk be close with God
With all the hopes made new.
So purer light shall mark the road
Leading to the Lamb.

1472 Louise & Nathan Fellingham
Copyright © 2000 Thankyou Music

O GOD OF LOVE, I come to You again,
Knowing I'll find mercy.
I can't explain all the things I see,
But I'll trust in You.
In every moment You are there,
Watching over, You hear my prayer.
You go before me, You're behind me,
Nothing's hidden from You.

How good it is to be loved by You,
How good it is.
(Repeat)

O God of strength,
Your hand is on my life,
Bringing peace to me.
You know my frame,
You know how I am made,
You planned all my days.
Hand of mercy, hand of love,
Giving power to overcome.
If all beneath me falls away,
I know that You are God.

Who can stand against us?
In my weakness You are strong.
Your word is everlasting,
I will praise You, faithful One.

1473 James Gregory
Copyright © 2000 Thankyou Music

OH FALLEN ONE, covered now in shame,
He is your hope, He is your life.
Though He should judge,
His anger turns away;
Rise from the dust, beautiful one.

Don't be afraid,
For you're not left alone;
His heart of love is broken for you.
Your Father cares
For all your children now,
Arise in His name, beautiful one.

Arise and shine, your glory has come,
Arise and shine, your glory has come,
Arise and shine,
He is calling you by name;
Though your walls have fallen down,
He'll build you up again.

Lift up your eyes,
Many come to see
The splendour your God has given to you.
Could each of your saints
Become a thousand saints?
Rise up and praise, beautiful one.

So let Your salvation come,
For Your glory, Lord.
Set the captives free, we pray;
These souls are Your reward.

1474 Brenton Brown
Copyright © 1999 Vineyard Songs (UK/Eire)/
Adm. by CopyCare

OH KNEEL ME DOWN AGAIN,
Here at Your feet;
Show me how much You love humility.
Oh Spirit, be the star that leads me to
The humble heart of love I see in You.

You are the God of the broken,
The friend of the weak;
You wash the feet of the weary,
Embrace the ones in need.
I want to be like You, Jesus,
To have this heart in me.
You are the God of the humble,
You are the humble King.

1475 Doug Horley
Copyright © 1997 Thankyou Music

OI, OI, WE ARE GONNA PRAISE THE LORD.

Oi, oi, we are gonna praise the Lord.
Oi, oi, we are gonna praise the Lord.
He's an exciting, powerising, c-colossal,
Humungous-mungous God!

But it's sometimes hard to understand
That the God who made the earth and man
Would point a finger down from heaven and
 shout:
'Hey you! I love you.
Hey you! I love you.
Hey you, you!
I love you', but it's true!

1476 Matt Redman
Copyright © 1999 Thankyou Music

O JESUS, SON OF GOD,

So full of grace and truth,
The Father's saving Word:
So wonderful are You.
The angels longed to see,
And prophets searched to find
The glory we have seen revealed.

You shone upon the earth,
But who will understand?
You came unto Your own,
But who will recognise?
Your birth was prophesied,
For You were the Messiah,
Who came and walked upon the earth.
Your glory we have seen,
The one and only King,
And now You're living in our hearts.

Light of the world, Light of the world,
Light of the world, You shine upon us.
Light of the world, Light of the world,
Light of the world, You shine upon us.

In You all things were made,
And nothing without You;
In heaven and on earth,
All things are held in You.
And yet You became flesh,
Living as one of us,
Under the shadow of the cross,
Where through the blood You shed,
You have made peace again,
Peace for the world that God so loves.

1477 Martyn Layzell
Copyright © 1998 Thankyou Music

O LORD, I AM DEVOTED TO YOU,

All that I am I give You,
Nothing do I withhold.
I am nothing without You,
All my hope is upon You,
Simply telling You I am Yours,
I am Yours.

Jesus, may my devotion be pleasing,
Expressed through this song I am singing,
Pouring my heart out to You, only You.
You are the reason for living, I'm
breathing:
My refuge, my strength and my healing,
So I give my heart unto You,
Only You.

Every earthly distraction
Fades away to the background,
I'm content just to be with You.
Jesus, You satisfy my longing,
To You do I cry, I'm coming,
Kneeling before Your throne,
At Your throne.

1478 Andrew & Shirley Rogers
Copyright © 2000 Thankyou Music

O LORD, OUR LORD, Your name is great

And greatly to be praised.
In heaven and the universe,
Your glory is displayed.
Every knee must bow to You
And every tongue confess:
You are Lord, the Son of God,
Risen from the dead.

You're Jesus, Ruler of the universe.
Majestic is Your name in all the earth.
Kingdoms rise, kingdoms fall,
You are still the Lord of all.
Majestic is Your name
Here on earth.

When I see the moon and stars
Created by Your breath;
Why did You consider me
Worthy of Your death?
When I was the guilty one
You took away my shame:
When I called, You hid me in
The refuge of Your name.

1479 Brian Houston
Copyright © 2000 Thankyou Music

O LORD, WHEN I WAKE UP in the morning,
Let my mouth be filled with praise for You.
O Lord, when I go out in the evening,
Let my mouth be filled with praise for You.
That all might know, yeah,
And many might see, yeah,
That You're my Lord.

Fill me with a spirit of boldness, O my God,
And come and take all of my shame;
That I might see temptation
Melt before my eyes
And watch the demons flee in Jesus' name,
As we lift high the name.

Lift high the name of the Lord.
Lift high the name of the Lord.
That many might know,
That many might see my Lord.

O Lord, when I'm stressed and feeling tired,
Let my mouth be filled with praise to You.
O Lord, when I'm pressed on every side,
Let my mouth be filled with praise to You.
That all might know, yeah,
And many might see, yeah,
That You are Lord.

1480 Jonathan James (Abundant Life Ministries,
Bradford, England)
Copyright © 2002 Thankyou Music

O LORD, YOU ARE FIRST IN MY LIFE;
For You I live as a sacrifice,
Holy in Your sight, pleasing to Your heart,
As I put my trust in You.

Precious Jesus, You paid such a cost,
That I may know Your love,
Your grace, Your touch;
With everything I am,
I want to know You more,
My heart is open to You.

As I seek You, Lord,
You draw me nearer.

I am Yours, Lord, I am Yours,
Completely abandoned to You.
I am Yours, Lord, I am Yours,
Wholly devoted to You.

1481 Stuart Townend
Copyright © 1999 Thankyou Music

**O MY SOUL, ARISE AND BLESS YOUR
    MAKER,**
For He is your Master and your Friend.
Slow to wrath but rich and tender mercy:
Worship the Saviour, Jesus.

King of grace, His love is overwhelming;
Bread of Life, He's all I'll ever need,
For His blood has purchased me forever:
Bought at the cross of Jesus.

And I will sing for all my days
Of heaven's love come down.
Each breath I take will speak His praise
Until He calls me home.

When I wake, I know that He is with me;
When I'm weak, I know that He is strong.
Though I fall, His arm is there to lean on:
Safe on the Rock of Jesus.

Stir in me the songs that You are singing;
Fill my gaze with things as yet unseen.
Give me faith to move in works of power,
Making me more like Jesus.
CHORUS
Then one day I'll see Him as He sees me,
Face to face, the Lover and the loved;
No more words, the longing will be over:
There with my precious Jesus.

1482 Kristyn Lennox & Keith Getty
Copyright © 2002 Thankyou Music

ONCE I WAS FAR AWAY,
But now my life is found in You.
Once I was without hope,
But now I have a vision of heaven.

Fallen from grace;
By faith lifted up;
Now I believe

No height, no depth can keep us
From the love of Christ.
No life, no death, no trial
Can tear us from
The love of God in Christ.

How wonderful the love
Our Father God has given us,
That we could still be called
Children of God.

1483 Sydney Carter
Copyright © 1971 Stainer & Bell Ltd

ONE MORE STEP ALONG THE WORLD I GO,
One more step along the world I go,
From the old things to the new,
Keep me travelling along with You.

And it's from the old I travel to the new,
Keep me travelling along with You.

Round the corners of the world I turn,
More and more about the world I learn.
All the new things that I see,
You'll be looking at along with me.

As I travel through the bad and good,
Keep me travelling the way I should.
Where I see no way to go,
You'll be telling me the way, I know.

Give me courage when the world is rough,
Keep me loving though the world is tough.
Leap and sing in all I do,
Keep me travelling along with You.

You are older than the world can be,
You are younger than the life in me.
Ever old and ever new,
Keep me travelling along with You.

1484 James Gregory
Copyright © 2000 Thankyou Music

ONE SACRIFICE AND I AM FREE,
The cross of Christ my victory,
And on this grace I do believe, yes I believe.
Jesus, in death You set me free,
Taking the punishment for me,
It is Your blood that covers me, yes I believe.

And because of what this love has done
My heart is filled with praise.

And so I lift my voice to You,
Pouring out all this love on You.
What can I give for all You've done for
me?
I know the Saviour lives today,
Heaven and earth may pass away,
But I know Your love will never fail.

And every day I live, I vow to follow You.

1485 Paul Oakley
Copyright © 2000 Thankyou Music

ONE THING I ASK, one thing I seek,
To see Your face, to gaze upon Your beauty,
To search behind the eyes of love.

To spend my days within the veil,
Where the purity and light pour over me,
And I am changed.

I gaze on the One who so desired
Friendship with one as low as me.
You left behind Your throne
So I'll sing of Your love (sing of Your love).

All I held close I now let go.
All else is loss compared to knowing You,
And I am changed.

The King who became the sacrifice,
Broken and cursed upon the tree,
The Saviour of my soul,
Hallelujah, hallelujah.

1486 Evan Rogers
Copyright © 2000 Thankyou Music

ONE THING I HAVE BEEN ASKING,
One thing I am looking for:
To see Your glory and beauty,
To know Your presence, Lord.

You're the desire of my heart,
And You are all that I want;
You're the desire of my heart,
And You are all that I want.

You have all my attention,
You are the One I'm living for;
In You I find satisfaction,
You are mine and I am Yours.

I am wanting You,
I am needing You much more, Lord.
You have won my heart,
You've given me all that You've got,
Your love was demonstrated on the cross.
Thank You, Lord!

1487 Dave Bilbrough
Copyright © 1999 Thankyou Music

ONE VOICE, one mind, one will to see
The heart of God revealed in power.
Let every nation, tribe and tongue
Come seek the Lord and His great love.

Send a revival, send a revival,
Send a revival, we pray.
Send a revival, send a revival,
Send a revival, we pray.

We will not cease, we will not rest
Until the Prince of Peace is seen.
As God with us, Emmanuel,
The hope of all humanity.

A vision burns within my soul
That all the world will come to know
The healing found at Calvary,
That place where truth and mercy meet.

I hear a sound across the earth;
It tells me that the time is near.
An anthem lifting up His name:
Make straight a path – prepare the way.

1488 James Taylor
Copyright © 2000 Thankyou Music

ONLY YOU can replace
Rags for riches pure as gold,
And Your mercy saved my soul,
There's none like You.

At Your name demons flee,
Mountains tremble in Your sight,
But You love me like a friend,
There's none like You.

> *Nothing compares to You,*
> *You're the One we love.*
> *Send down Your holy fire*
> *Over all the earth.*
> (Repeat)

You have paid such a cost,
So much more than can be won:
God, You gave Your only Son,
There's none like You.

So we'll bow to the cross
Where the tears of heaven fall.
You have heard the sinner's call:
There's none like You.

1489 James Gregory
Copyright © 2002 Thankyou Music

OPENING OUR HEARTS TO YOU,
Focusing our eyes on You,
Lifting up our hands to You,
Singing out this song for You.
Praises that will fill the skies,
Raising You over our lives,
Lifting up the Saviour high.

We give You the highest praise,
We give You the highest praise,
We give You the highest praise,
We give You the highest praise.

You are so amazing, Lord,
A beautiful and mighty God,
Compassionate and merciful,
Glorious and powerful.
King over the universe,
Wonderfully in love with us,
Passionate about the earth.

All glory, honour, worship, praise,
With hands held high and voices raised,
We offer up our hearts again to You.
(Repeat)

1490 Paul Baloche
Copyright © 1997 Integrity Hosanna! Music/
Sovereign Music UK

OPEN THE EYES OF MY HEART, Lord,
Open the eyes of my heart.
I want to see You,
I want to see You.
(Repeat)

To see You high and lifted up,
Shining in the light of Your glory.
Pour out Your power and love,
As we sing holy, holy, holy.

Holy, holy, holy,
Holy, holy,holy,
Holy holy holy,
I want to see You.

1491 Paul Oakley
Copyright © 1998 Thankyou Music

OPEN UP THE GATES OF HEAVEN.
Open up the gates of heaven.
Open up the gates of heaven.
Open up the gates of heaven,

And let Your river flow,
And let new mercies fall like rain;
Oh, let me know Your presence.
You are all I need;
Let all earthly passion fade away,

> *('Cause) all I want is to know You more.*
> *All I want is to meet with You in this place.*
> *All I want is to be with You,*
> *To feel Your embrace.*

1492 Chris Tomlin, Louie Giglio & Jesse Reeves
Copyright © 2000 worshiptogether.com songs/
Six Steps Music/Adm. by Kingsway Music

OPEN UP THE SKIES of mercy,
Rain down the cleansing flood;
Healing waters rise around us;
Hear our cries, Lord, let 'em rise.

It's Your kindness, Lord, that leads us to
repentance;
Your favour, Lord, is our desire.
It's Your beauty, Lord, that makes us stand
in silence,
And Your love, Your love is better than
life.

We can feel Your mercy falling;
You are turning our hearts back again.
Hear our praises rise to heaven;
Draw us near, Lord, meet us here.

1493 Matt Redman
Copyright © 1999 Thankyou Music

O SACRED KING, O holy King,
How can I honour You rightly,
Honour that's right for Your name?
O sacred Friend, O holy Friend,
I don't take what You give lightly,
Friendship instead of disgrace.

For it's the mystery of the universe,
You're the God of holiness,
Yet You welcome souls like me.
And with the blessing of Your Father's heart,
You discipline the ones You love,
There's kindness in Your majesty.
Jesus, those who recognise Your power,
Know just how wonderful You are,
That You draw near.

1494 Dave Bilbrough
Copyright © 1999 Thankyou Music

O TASTE AND SEE that the Lord is good.
O taste and see that the Lord is good.

He is a mighty God,
His ways are higher than ours;
There's nothing impossible for Him.
The future is in His hands.
We're a part of His perfect plan,
And we can do all things
Through the power of His love.

1495 D.R. Edwards. adapt. by Graham Kendrick
Words in this version Copyright © 2001 Make
Way Music

O, THE LOVE OF GOD IS BOUNDLESS,
Perfect, causeless, full and free!
Doubts have vanished, fears are groundless,
Now I know that love to me.
Love, the source of all my blessing,
Love that set itself on me.
Love that gave the sinless Victim,
Love told out at Calvary.

O, the cross of Christ is wondrous!
There I learn God's heart to me;
'Midst the silent, deepening darkness
'God is light' I also see.
Holy claims of justice finding
Full expression in that scene;
Light and love alike are telling
What His woe and suffering means.

O, the sight of heaven is glorious!
Man in righteousness is there.
Once the victim, now victorious,
Jesus lives in glory fair!
Him, who met the claims of glory
And the need of ruined man
On the cross, O wondrous story!
God has set at His right hand.

O, what rest of soul in seeing
Jesus on His Father's throne!
Yes, what peace forever flowing
From God's rest in His own Son!
Gazing upward into heaven,
Reading glory in His face,
Knowing that 'tis He, once given
On the cross to take my place.

1496 Stuart Townend & Gary Sadler
Copyright © 2000 Integrity's Hosanna! Music/
Sovereign Music UK & Thankyou Music

OUR GOD IS STRONG AND MIGHTY,
He's lifting up a shout.
It's rolling down like thunder:
Can you feel it shake the ground?
And every stronghold trembles
As we hear the Lion roar!

He's breaking out.
(The Lord our God is breaking out.)
The Lord our God is breaking out.
(The Lord our God)
He's breaking out!

He's rising in this nation,
He's coming into view;
Go tell it in the city
What Jesus' power can do.
We're losing our religion –
He's even greater than we thought!

O God of mercy, God of love,
Come show us the glory of Your name.
We're touched by the passion of Your heart,
And nothing will ever be the same,
Nothing will ever be the same,
Don't let me ever be the same.

Come do a work within me,
Let me see You as You are;
And make the cause of heaven
The obsession of my heart,
Till every tribe and nation
Bows in worship to the King.

1497 Viola Grafstrom
Copyright © 1998 Thankyou Music

OUR MASTER, OUR SAVIOUR,
You are Lord, our King.
Our Master, our Saviour,
We give our praise to our King,
To our King.

You're the everlasting Father,
The beginning and the end.
There is no one that can take Your place,
There is no other name.

1498 Brenton Brown
Copyright © 1998 Vineyard Songs (UK/Eire)/
Adm. by CopyCare

OVER ALL THE EARTH,
You reign on high,
Every mountain stream,
Every sunset sky.
But my one request,
Lord, my only aim
Is that You'd reign in me again.

Lord, reign in me,
Reign in Your power;
Over all my dreams,
In my darkest hour.
You are the Lord of all I am,
So won't You reign in me again?

Over every thought,
Over every word,
May my life reflect the beauty of my Lord;
'Cause You mean more to me
Than any earthly thing,
So won't You reign in me again?

1499 Noel Robinson
Copyright © 2000 Thankyou Music

OVER, OVER,
The joy of the Lord is running over.
Over, over,
The joy of the Lord is running over.

Let me tell you of the supernatural joy
That You can find in Him,
The man called Jesus.
He'll take away the sorrow of this life
That brings so much sadness,
Give you overflowing joy
That no man can ever, ever touch, yeah.

Weeping may endure;
Joy comes in the morning.
Weeping may endure;
Joy comes!

1500 Kevin Mayhew
Copyright © 1976 Kevin Mayhew Ltd

PEACE, PERFECT PEACE
Is the gift of Christ our Lord.
Peace, perfect peace,
Is the gift of Christ our Lord.
Thus, says the Lord,
Will the world know My friends.
Peace, perfect peace,
Is the gift of Christ our Lord.

Love, perfect love…

Faith, perfect faith…

Hope, perfect hope…

Joy, perfect joy…

1501 Russell Fragar
Copyright © 1998 Russell Fragar/
Hillsong Publishing/Kingsway Music

PRAISE HIM, YOU HEAVENS
And all that's above.
Praise Him, you angels
And heavenly hosts.
Let the whole earth praise Him.
Praise Him, the sun, moon
And bright shining stars.
Praise Him, you heavens
And waters and skies.
Let the whole earth praise Him.

Great in power, great in glory,
Great in mercy, King of heaven.
Great in battle, great in wonder,
Great in Zion, King over all the earth.

1502 David Gate
Copyright © 1999 Thankyou Music

PRAISES,
For all that You've done I'll sing praises,
For sending Your Son who would save me,
Pouring out grace at the cross
Where You died for me.
Mercies,
Through all of my life I've seen mercies,
Through hardship and strife You are with me,
By my side, You are good,
So good to me.

Through Your death You brought me life,
Took my shame, clothed me in white.

> *Lord, here I am, amazed again,*
> *That You would die to save a friend.*
> *You clear my sin and pay the cost,*
> *So on my knees I'll stay,*
> *At the foot of the cross.*

Worship,
Day after day I will worship,
For glory and grace, and for goodness,
With all of my life I will be Your living praise.
And Jesus,
I'll always look unto Jesus,
For guidance and strength and my focus,
Trying to live how You want Your child to be.

1503 Martin E. Leckebusch /
Chorus words: Graham Kendrick
Copyright © 2000 Kevin Mayhew Ltd
Chorus words Copyright © 2002 Make Way Music

PRAISE TO CHRIST, THE LORD INCARNATE,
Gift of God by human birth:
He it is who came among us,
Shared our life and showed our worth;
Ours the turmoil He encountered,
Ours the fight He made His own;
Now within our hearts His Spirit
Makes His way of freedom known.

> *Praise to Christ our Saviour and our King.*
> *Praise to Christ our King.*

Praise to Christ, the Man of Sorrows,
Tasting death for our release:
His the cup of bitter anguish,
Ours the pardon, ours the peace;
His the blood that seals forgiveness,
Ours the weight of guilt He bore –
So by death and resurrection
Christ has opened heaven's door.

Praise to Christ, the Priest eternal:
Still for us He intercedes;
Still He sees our pains and problems –
How He understands our needs!
Yesterday, today, forever,
Always He remains the same:
Pledged to bring us to the Father,
Strong in grace and free from blame.

1504 Paul Crouch & David Mudie
Copyright © 1991 Daybreak Music Ltd

PRAYER IS LIKE A TELEPHONE
For us to talk to Jesus.
Prayer is like a telephone
For us to talk to God.
Prayer is like a telephone
For us to talk to Jesus.
Pick it up and use it every day.

We can shout out loud,
We can whisper softly,
We can make no noise at all.
But He'll always hear our call.

1505 Dave Bilbrough
Copyright © 2000 Thankyou Music

PREPARE THE WAY of the Lord,
Prepare the way of the Lord.
Prepare the way of the Lord,
Prepare the way of the Lord.

Majestic in holiness,
Awesome in glory,
Doing wonders, this is our God.
We will not be silenced
From speaking His word.
We cry to the nations:

All authority is invested
In the name of Jesus,
And at the sounding of that name,
At the sounding of that name
He will arise.

1506 Evelyn Tarner
Copyright © 1967 Sacred Songs/Word Music/
Adm. by CopyCare

REJOICE IN THE LORD ALWAYS
And again I say rejoice.
Rejoice in the Lord always
And again I say rejoice.

Rejoice, rejoice, and again I say rejoice.
Rejoice, rejoice, and again I say rejoice.

1507
Augustus M. Toplady (1740–78)
adapt. by Graham Kendrick
Words in this version Copyright © 2001 Make
Way Music

ROCK OF AGES, cleft for me,
Let me hide myself in Thee.
Let the water and the blood
From Your wounded side which flowed,
Be of sin the double cure,
Cleanse me from its guilt and power.

My Rock (my Rock),
My Jesus, my Rock.
My Rock (my Rock),
My Jesus, my Rock.

Not the labours of my hands
Can fulfil Your law's demands.
Could my zeal no respite know,
Could my tears forever flow,
All for sin could not atone.
You must save and You alone.

Nothing in my hand I bring,
Simply to Your cross I cling.
Naked, come to You for dress,
Helpless, look to You for grace.
Foul, I to the fountain fly:
Wash me, Saviour, or I die.

While I draw this fleeting breath,
When my eyelids close in death,
When I soar to worlds unknown,
See You on Your judgement throne,
Rock of Ages, cleft for me,
Let me hide myself in Thee.

1508
Sue Rinaldi, Caroline Bonnett & Steve Bassett
Copyright © 2001 Thankyou Music

SACRED, holy, pure,
Lord of space and time,
Dwells in perfect light,
Radiance sublime.
Sacred holy songs
Rise on wings of praise;
All creation rings
With echoes of Your grace.

And oh, my grateful heart rejoices at Your
name.
And oh, my grateful heart rejoices at Your
name.

Sacred, risen Son,
Peerless Lamb of God;
Mercy, grace and peace
Rolling like a flood.
Promise forged in pain,
Forgiveness bought by blood;
Sealed with sacred words
From the mouth of God.

1509
Charlie Hall
Copyright © 1997 worshiptogether.com songs/
Six Steps Music/Adm. by Kingsway Music

SALVATION, SPRING UP from the ground,
Lord, rend the heavens and come down.
Seek the lost and heal the lame;
Jesus, bring glory to Your name.
Let all the prodigals run home,
All of creation waits and groans.
Lord, we've heard of Your great fame;
Father, cause all to shout Your name.

Stir up our hearts, O God;
Open our spirits to awe who You are.
Put a cry in us
So deep inside,
That we cannot find
The words we need,
We just weep and cry out to You.

1510
Tim Sherrington
Copyright © 1998 Thankyou Music

SEARCH MY SOUL, and pierce my heart
With a fire that burns from Your eyes.
And drive me on to the reason for living,
That is just for You,
That is just for You.

How long must I wait for Your coming?
Come quickly, Lord,
'Cause You're the only answer.
And drive me on to the reason for living,
That is just for You,
That is just for You.

Let Your kingdom come,
Let Your will be done,
Let Your rain pour out on my life.
Let Your kingdom come,
Let Your will be done,
Let Your rain drench my life and do Your
will.

Come and break the chains
That hold me back, Lord,
From dancing in Your light
And being a fool for You.
And I'm running back to the reason for living,
That is just for You,
That is just for You.

1511 Robert Critchley
Copyright © 1996 Thankyou Music

SEE HOW THE FATHER opens the heavens
To honour His Son.
See how the Spirit descends like a dove
Upon His belovèd One.
This the Lamb of God
Who takes away the sins of the world.
Grace has appeared to heal the nations,
Christ has been given to set us free,
To Him be the glory forevermore.

> *To Jesus be glory forevermore.*
> *To Jesus be glory forevermore.*

See how the Father opens the heavens,
Revealing His Son.
Angels and elders and saints without number
Worship the risen One.
And with a shout they proclaim,
'Worthy is the Lamb who was slain;
To Him be all power and riches and wisdom,
To Him be all the honour, dominion and
    praise,
To Him be the glory forevermore.'

Can you hear the Father saying,
'I am so pleased, just look at My Son,
Just look at My Son'?

1512 Dave Bilbrough
Copyright © 2002 Thankyou Music

SEND YOUR SPIRIT, *(×3)*
O Lord, we pray.

Light our darkness, *(×3)*
O Lord, we pray.

Move in power, *(×3)*
O Lord, we pray.

For the honour of Your name, *(×6)*
O Lord.

1513 Marc James & Tré Sheppard
Copyright © 2001 Vineyard Songs (UK/Eire)/
Adm. by CopyCare

> **SHINE YOUR LIGHT ON US**
> *That all may see Your goodness.*
> *Shine Your face on us*
> *That all may see Your glory.*

Answer me when I call.
You are my only prayer.
When darkness is all around
I know You will be there.

Many are asking,
Who can show us something real?
Longing for hope
Beyond the pain of what they feel.
So I will go down on my knees and say:

I wanna be close to You,
That my life would tell Your story.
I wanna be one with You,
Changed by the light of Your glory.

1514 Taizé, music: Jacques Berthier (1923–94)
Copyright © 1982 Ateliers et Presses de Taizé

SING, PRAISE AND BLESS THE LORD.
Sing, praise and bless the Lord.
Peoples! Nations! Alleluia!

Laudate Dominum,
Laudate Dominum,
Omnes gentes, alleluia!

1515 Jacques Berthier (1923–94)
Copyright © Ateliers et Presses de Taizé

SING PRAISES, ALL YOU PEOPLES,
Sing praises to the Lord.
Sing praises, all you peoples,
Sing praises to the Lord.

Laudate omnes gentes,
Laudate Dominum.
Laudate omnes gentes,
Laudate Dominum.

1516 David Lyle Morris
Copyright © 2001 Thankyou Music

> **SING PRAISES TO OUR GOD**, *sing*
>   *praises.*
> *Sing praises to the King, sing praises.*
> (Repeat)

For God is King of all the earth,
Sing to Him a psalm of praise.
God reigns over the nations,
All our worship we will raise.
He's King of all the earth,
Bring to Him a joyful song.
He's Lord of all creation,
Seated on His holy throne.

Clap your hands, all you nations,
Shout to God with cries of joy,
How awesome is the Lord most high.
Clap your hands, all creation,
Cry to God who made us all,
The great King over all the world.

1517
Robert Johnson, altd Lex Loizides
Copyright © 1998 Thankyou Music

SOLDIERS OF OUR GOD, ARISE!
The day is drawing nearer;
Shake the slumber from your eyes,
The light is growing clearer.
Sit no longer idly by
While the heedless millions die.
O, lift the blood-stained banner high,
And take the field for Jesus.

Save the lost! Save the lost!
Spend your might for them;
Give your life for them.
Save the lost! Save the lost!
Don't back down on it;
Win your crown in it,
Soldiers of our God,
Soldiers of our God.

See the brazen hosts of hell
Their art and power employing,
More than human tongue can tell
The blood-bought souls destroying.
See on ruin's hell-bound road
Victims groan beneath their load;
Go forward, O you sons of God,
And dare or die for Jesus.

Warriors of the risen King,
Great army of salvation,
Spread His fame, His praises sing
And conquer every nation.
Raise the glorious standard higher,
Work for victory, never tire;
O, forward march with blood and fire,
And win the world for Jesus.

1518
Martyn Layzell
Copyright © 2002 Thankyou Music

SOVEREIGN LORD, over all,
You are reigning forever.
Worship flows from our lips,
We have come for just one glimpse.

And we sing hallelujah,
Hallelujah, hallelujah.

Majesty, reign in me,
Your right hand enfolding me.
Earth applaud, heavens sing
At the sight of Christ the King.

Lord of lords, now enthroned,
Who can stand in Your presence?
Fire of love, holy One,
You burn brighter than the sun.

1519
Tim Sherrington
Copyright © 2001 Thankyou Music

SPIRIT, MOVE ON THIS LAND,
Take Your people in Your hands.
We're waiting for the day,
The day You come again.
Your Spirit is coming to give to the poor;
So Father, take our lives and shine.

Revival in our land,
Won't rest until we see
Revival in our land.
(Repeat)

1520
Ian White
Copyright © 1997 Thankyou Music

SPIRIT OF THE LORD, come down among us now;
Minister new life to bones grown dry.
Something in our heart cries out to be made whole:
The touch of healing love.

Give us just a glimpse of God, of Jesus' heart,
Open ears to hear the voice say, 'Come':
Look up, look up, look up and see
The light of healing love.

1521
Paul Oakley & Martin Cooper
Copyright © 2001 Thankyou Music

STANDING ON HOLY GROUND,
Mercy and grace I've found.
I'm here before Your throne now,
By a new and living way.
Jesus, I come to You.
I lift up my eyes to You.
How You've comforted me,
And now I long to see Your face.

You are my strength, my song;
You are my shield, my Redeemer.
You are my hope, my salvation,
And my God.
(First time)
I'll always bring my praise to You,
O God.

(Second time)
So I will sing to You,
Beautiful things You have done.
Great is Your name in Zion,
Holy One.
I'll always bring my praise to You,
I'll always bring my praise to You,
I'll always bring my praise to You,
O God.

1522

Taizé, music: Jacques Berthier (1923–94)
Copyright © 1980 Ateliers et Presses de Taizé

STAY WITH ME,
Remain here with me,
Watch and pray;
Watch and pray.

1523

David Lyle Morris & Liz Morris
Copyright © 2000 Thankyou Music

SURELY OUR GOD *is the God of gods,*
And the Lord of kings,
The revealer of mysteries.
(Repeat)

He changes the times and the seasons,
He gives rhythm to the tides;
He knows what is hidden
In the darkest of places,
Brings the shadows into His light.

I'll praise You always, my Father,
You are Lord of heaven and earth.
You hide Your secrets
From the 'wise' and the learnèd,
And reveal them to this, Your child.

Thank You for sending Your only Son,
We may know the mystery of God;
He opens the treasures
Of wisdom and knowledge
To the humble, not to the proud.

1524

Noel & Tricia Richards
Copyright © 2000 Thankyou Music

TAKE ME TO YOUR SACRED PLACE,
How I long to see Your face.
I'll be lost in Your embrace
And be loved, and be loved by You.

Take me where Your glory shines,
Where Your holy fire burns.
Purify this heart of mine,
I surrender my life to You.

> *Draw me, draw me*
> *To Your sacred place.*
> *Draw me, draw me*
> *Till I see Your face.*

1525

Robin Mark
Copyright © 1998 Thankyou Music

TAKE US TO THE RIVER,
Take us there in unity to sing
A song of Your salvation
To win this generation for our King.
A song of Your forgiveness,
For it is with grace that river flows;
Take us to the river
In the city of our God.

Take us to Your throne room,
Give us ears to hear the cry of heaven;
For that cry is mercy,
Mercy to the fallen sons of man:
For mercy it has triumphed,
Triumphed over judgement by Your blood;
Take us to the throne room
In the city of our God.

> *For the Spirit of the Sovereign Lord is*
> *   upon us:*
> *This is the year of the Lord.*
> *The Spirit of the Sovereign Lord is upon*
> *   us,*
> *This is the year of the Lord.*

Take us to the mountain,
Lift us in the shadow of Your hands;
Is this Your mighty angel,
Who stands astride the ocean and the land?
For in his hand Your mercy
Showers on a dry and barren place;
Take us to the mountain
In the city of our God.

1526

David Gate
Copyright © 2001 Thankyou Music

TEACH ME OF YOUR WAYS,
To honour You with all I have,
And that I learn to say:
'Not my will, but Yours, my Lord.'

> *O Jesus, be glorified*
> *In all of my life.*
> *It's all about You,*
> *And the worship You're due.*
> *So help me to change,*
> *Mould me like clay;*
> *Lord, have Your way,*
> *Lord, have Your way with me.*

Lord, I long to be
A faithful child who honours You.
So Jesus, be in me,
Let Your light shine through me now.

1527 Dave Bilbrough
Copyright © 1998 Thankyou Music

TELL THE WORLD that Jesus is risen,
Let His praise encircle the globe;
Make it known among all the nations
That Jesus is alive!

From the cradle to the grave,
From a stable to a cross,
His life was offered up in sacrifice for us.
He came from heaven's throne
To seek and save the lost;
To reconcile us back to God.

No eye has seen, no ear has heard what He's
prepared;
His resurrection means His life is ours to
share.
The greatest miracle of all has taken place;
Christ is risen, He is Lord!

1528 Darlene Zschech
Copyright © 2000 Darlene Zschech/
Hillsong Publishing/Kingsway Music

THANK YOU FOR THE CROSS, LORD,
Thank You for the price You paid.
Bearing all my sin and shame,
In love You came
And gave amazing grace.

Thank You for this love, Lord,
Thank You for the nail-pierced hands.
Washed me in Your cleansing flow,
Now all I know:
Your forgiveness and embrace.

Worthy is the Lamb
Seated on the throne,
Crown You now with many crowns.
You reign victorious,
High and lifted up,
Jesus, Son of God,
The darling of heaven crucified.
Worthy is the Lamb.
Worthy is the Lamb.

1529 Paul Booth
Copyright © 1999 Thankyou Music

THANK YOU, LORD, FOR YOUR LOVE TO ME.
By Your truth You have set me free.
Through the cross I can enter in.
What seemed impossible till I let You
Wash away my sin,
Take away all shame
By the life-giving blood
Of Jesus, my Redeemer.

Holy, I stand before You,
Truly, I am blameless in Your sight.
Righteous, a royal robe I don't deserve,
Yet You choose to clothe me still,
Precious mercy.

Such mercy, such grace,
Such kindness to save
Even a sinner like me.
I'll love You, I'll serve You,
I'll praise You forever,
Thank You, Lord, for Your love to me.

1530 Paul Oakley & Megamix Kids
Copyright © 2001 Thankyou Music

THANK YOU, LORD, YOU LOVE US,
Thank You, Lord, You care.
Thank You, Lord, You made us,
Thank You, Lord, You're there.
Thank You for forgiveness,
Your gift of life to me.
Thank You for Your faithfulness,
You're always, always, always, always
Good to me.

So we really want to say,
'We love You,'
We really want to shout,
'You're the best!'
We're gonna bring our praise to You,
King of kings and my best friend.
(Repeat)
Oh yeah!

1531 Matt Redman
Copyright © 1999 Thankyou Music

THANK YOU, THANK YOU FOR THE BLOOD
that You shed,
Standing in its blessing we sing these
freedom songs.
Thank You, thank You for the battle You won,
Standing in Your victory we sing salvation
songs,
We sing salvation's song.

You have opened the way to the Father,
When before we could never have come.
Jesus, count us as Yours now forever,
As we sing these freedom songs.

We sing of all You've done,
We sing of all You've done,
We sing of all You've done for us,
Won for us, paid for us.
(Repeat)

1532 Stuart Townend
Copyright © 2000 Thankyou Music

THE BIRDS DON'T WORRY,
The flowers don't fret,
The trees don't hurry
For the food they get;
For God looks after
The things He's made:
They can depend on Him.

So don't you worry 'bout the things you
*   need,*
For clothes to wear or for food to eat;
But seek His kingdom and the rest will
*   come:*
You can depend on Him.

The hills don't grumble,
The stars don't cry,
The sun doesn't tumble
From the big, blue sky;
For God has set everything in place:
They can depend on Him.

You can't live longer by worrying more,
You can't get taller than you were before;
So seek His kingdom and the rest will
*   come:*
You can depend on Him.

1533 Chris Tomlin & Jesse Reeves
Copyright © 2002 worshiptogether.com songs/
Six Steps Music/Adm. by Kingsway Music

THE CROSS BEFORE ME, the world behind;
No turning back, raise the banner high:
It's not for me, it's all for You.
Let the heavens shake and split the sky,
Let the people clap their hands and cry:
It's not for us, it's all for You.

Not to us,
But to Your name be the glory.
(Repeat)

Our hearts unfold before Your throne,
The only place for those who know:
It's not for us, it's all for You.
Send Your holy fire on this offering,
Let our worship burn for the world to see:
It's not for us, it's all for You.

The earth is shaking, the mountains shouting:
It's all for You.
The waves are crashing, the sun is raging:
It's all for You.

The universe spinning and singing:
It's all for You.
Your children dancing, dancing, dancing:
It's all for You, it's all for You.
My all for You, my all for You.

1534 Mark Pendergrass
Copyright © Garden Valley Music/Birdwing Music/
BMG Songs Inc./EMI Christian Music Publishing/
Adm. by CopyCare

THE GREATEST THING IN ALL MY LIFE is
    knowing You;
The greatest thing in all my life is knowing
    You;
I want to know You more;
I want to know You more.
The greatest thing in all my life is knowing
    You.

The greatest thing in all my life is loving You;
The greatest thing in all my life is loving You;
I want to love You more;
I want to love You more.
The greatest thing in all my life is loving You.

The greatest thing in all my life is serving
    You;
The greatest thing in all my life is serving
    You;
I want to serve You more;
I want to serve You more.
The greatest thing in all my life is serving
    You.

1535 David Ruis
Copyright © 2001 Vineyard Songs (Canada)/
Adm. by CopyCare

THE NARROW PATHWAY
Through the needle's eye,
I'm stepping forward
To the place I die.
For I know that You are faithful,
As we walk these fields of white.
To the waiting and the humble
Your kingdom comes.

The way of mercy
Takes me to the least,
Down the road of suffering
To the wedding feast.
For I know that You are faithful,
As we walk these fields of white.
To the weary and the hurting
Your kingdom comes.

1536 David Lyle Morris & Jussi Miettinen
Copyright © 2000 Thankyou Music

THE PEOPLE WHO WALK IN DARKNESS
Will see a great light,
For those who live in the land
Of the shadow of death,
The light will shine.

You will enlarge the nation,
And increase their joy,
So they delight in Your presence
As they will rejoice
At harvest time.

For to us a Child is born,
To us a Son is given,
And the government
Will be upon His shoulders.
Of His government and peace
There will always be increase;
There is no end to His kingdom.

He will be called Wonderful,
Counsellor, Mighty God,
Everlasting Father, Prince of Peace.
(Repeat)
The Prince of Peace.

For to us a Child is born,
To us a Son is given,
And the government
Will be upon Your shoulders.
Come to break our yoke of grief,
The bar across our shoulders;
Lord, smash the rod of our oppressors.

You will be called...

1537 Ed Pask
Copyright © 2001 Thankyou Music

THE PLACE WHERE YOU DWELL
Is where I want to be,
It's where angels in splendour
Worship the King.
And to Jesus in glory
Each voice raised in song:
Holy, holy, holy is the Lord.

In the light of Your presence
I find perfect peace,
And my heart shall adore You
And in You rejoice.
And to Jesus victorious
I lift up my song:
Worthy, worthy, worthy is the Lamb.

It's all for You, Jesus,
Only You, Jesus.
You are my song and my reason to sing;
You have set this heart free
To rise on the wings of Your praise.

1538 Gary Sadler
Copyright © 1998 Integrity's Hosanna! Music/
Sovereign Music UK

THE POWER OF YOUR LOVE is changing me,
Changing me, changing me.
O Lord, change me by the power of Your love.
(Repeat)

You've drawn me to Your side,
And what else can I do?
My heart is open wide,
My hands reach out to You.
I'm calling out for more;
I'm asking in Your name,
That by Your Spirit, Lord,
I will never be the same.

I'm singing out my praise,
I'm pouring out my thanks,
For the power of Your love is changing me.
I'm lifting up my voice,
I'm dancing in the joy,
For the power of Your love is changing me.

1539 Nathan Fellingham
Copyright © 2001 Thankyou Music

THERE IS A DAY
That all creation's waiting for,
A day of freedom and liberation for the earth.
And on that day
The Lord will come to meet His bride,
And when we see Him
In an instant we'll be changed.

The trumpet sounds
And the dead will then be raised
By His power,
Never to perish again.
Once only flesh,
Now clothed with immortality;
Death has now been
Swallowed up in victory.

We will meet Him in the air
And then we will be like Him,
For we will see Him, as He is,
Oh yeah!
Then all hurt and pain will cease,
And we'll be with Him forever,
And in His glory we will live,
Oh yeah, oh yeah!

So lift your eyes
To the things as yet unseen,
That will remain now
For all eternity.
Though trouble's hard
It's only momentary,
And it's achieving
Our future glory.

1540 James Taylor
Copyright © 1999 Thankyou Music

THERE IS A DEEPER LOVE TO KNOW,
There is a higher place where we can go.
There is a freedom at the cross,
There is a light that shines for all the world.

And I can't hold this joy inside,
I'm jumping in Your arms of mercy.

Everybody sing, everybody shout,
For the joy of the Lord
Is our strength forever.
Hey, everybody sing, everybody shout,
For the joy of the Lord is our strength.

There is a brighter day to come,
When all the world will bow down to Your
　Son.
And all the broken will rejoice,
Even the kings will say, 'You are the Lord'.

And we can't hold this joy inside,
We're dancing in Your arms of mercy.

1541 Kristyn Lennox & Keith Getty
Copyright © 2002 Thankyou Music

THERE IS A HIGHER THRONE
Than all this world has known,
Where faithful ones from every tongue
Will one day come.
Before the Son we'll stand,
Made faultless through the Lamb;
Believing hearts find promised grace:
Salvation comes.

Hear heaven's voices sing,
Their thunderous anthem rings
Through emerald courts and sapphire
　skies,
Their praises rise.
All glory, wisdom, power,
Strength, thanks and honour are
To God, our King who reigns on high
Forever more.

And there we'll find our home,
Our life before the throne;
We'll honour Him in perfect song
Where we belong.
He'll wipe each tear-stained eye,
As thirst and hunger die;
The Lamb becomes our Shepherd King:
We'll reign with Him.

1542 Graham Kendrick
Copyright © 2002 Make Way Music

THERE IS A HOPE SO SURE,
A promise so secure:
The mystery of God at last made known.
Treasures so vast appear,
All wisdom, knowledge here:
It's Christ in us, the hope of glory!

And the life that I now live,
No longer is my own,
Jesus lives in me, the hope of glory.
And each day I live,
No longer is my own,
Jesus lives in me, the hope of glory.

There is a life so true,
A life of love so pure,
For all our sin a perfect sacrifice.
And when that life was nailed,
On cruel cross impaled,
Our sinful flesh with Him was crucified.

There is a life so strong
That a whole world of wrong
And all the powers of hell could not defeat.
For Jesus rose again,
And if we died with Him,
With Him we'll rise to share His endless life.

1543 Nathan Fellingham
Copyright © 2001 Thankyou Music

THERE IS A NAME that's high over all.
There is a King seated on the throne.
And He's interceding for me,
So that I will be made holy,
And I know that in His love
I will stay.

What a Saviour is my Jesus,
He came down
So that I may go free.

There is a Man who walked on the earth,
The Word of God made known to us.
He's the image of the Father,
The Firstborn over creation,
Yet He suffered at the hands of those He saves.

What a Saviour is my Jesus,
He came down
So that I may go free.
How I love You, oh my Jesus,
You came down
So that I may go free.

1544 David Fellingham & Kim Morgan
Copyright © 2001 Thankyou Music

THERE IS A PASSION deep in my heart
To know You, Jesus.
There is a hunger deep in my soul
Only You can satisfy.
I hear You calling, drawing me closer,
I can't resist Your grace.
Almighty power and love so free,
Draw me to Your side.

And I'm lifted into Your presence,
Lifted into Your arms of love.
Lifted into Your presence,
Now has my soul found rest,
Now has my soul found rest.

I see Your face,
I feel Your touch;
Receive Your love,
I worship You.
(Repeat)

1545 Paul Oakley
Copyright © 1998 Thankyou Music

THERE IS A VOICE THAT MUST BE HEARD,
There is a song that must be sung;
There is a name that must be lifted high.
There is a treasure more than gold,
There is a King upon the throne;
There is One whose praise will fill the skies.

His name is Jesus, Friend of sinners,
Jesus, Jesus, Friend of mine.

There is a peace that calms our fears,
There is a love stronger than death;
There is a hope that goes beyond the grave.
There is a Friend who won't let go,
There is a heart that beats for you;
There is one name by which we are saved.

When I was captive to my fears,
You were the One who came to me,
You set me free.

1546 Robin Mark
Copyright © 1999 Integrity's Hosanna! Music/
Sovereign Music UK

THERE IS NO OTHER NAME
By which men can be saved,
There is no other name under heaven.
There is rest for my soul
And the wounded made whole,
And the captives set free and forgiven.

Such love as I had never known,
I've found in the grace that flowed to me
In my unrighteousness;
This is why my heart and soul and tongue
confess.

1547 Tim Hughes
Copyright © 2002 Thankyou Music

THERE MUST BE MORE than this:
O Breath of God, come breathe within.
There must be more than this:
Spirit of God, we wait for You.
Fill us anew, we pray;
Fill us anew, we pray.

Consuming fire, fan into flame
A passion for Your name.
Spirit of God, fall in this place.
Lord, have Your way,
Lord, have Your way with us.

Come like a rushing wind,
Clothe us with power from on high.
Now set the captives free;
Leave us abandoned to Your praise.
Lord, let Your glory fall;
Lord, let Your glory fall.

1548 Stuart Townend
Copyright © 2001 Thankyou Music

THERE'S A CALL to the people of Zion,
To arise and possess the land;
Every town has its heirs to the promise,
Every nation its sons of light.
We have stayed long enough on this mountain,
Now we're called to new realms of faith;
We are more than a temple of worship,
We're an army of praise!

We will go to every place,
Sharing mercy and preaching grace,
For the fields are white for harvest,
And labourers are few.
No place too dark, no soul too lost
For the power of the cross;
For His light will shine in darkness,
And many will believe,
So we will go.

We have drunk of the wine of His presence,
We have feasted upon His word;
Now we're hungry for works of power,
Now we're thirsty to share His love.
He will give us the ground that we walk on,
For the battle belongs to God;
Do not fear, for His grace is sufficient,
When we're weak, He is strong!

1549 Ken Riley
Copyright © 1999 Thankyou Music

THERE'S A CALLING TO THE NATIONS
To make ready in Your name,
To take up the yoke of Jesus
And proclaim the coming day.
There's a pouring of Your Spirit
As our old men dream Your dreams;
Prophesy through sons and daughters,
Come envision us again.

You're the Word and the Word is Truth,
You're the Promise that was born in You,
And a wave of expectation fills my soul!

> *All over the world we're singing,*
> *All over the world there's praise*
> *To the King of our salvation,*
> *And the Author of our faith.*
> *All over the world we're dancing,*
> *All over the world there's joy,*
> *We've called upon Your name*
> *And we are saved.*

Can it be this generation
That will hear revival's song,
As Your Spirit of creation
Comes awakening the lost?
Let the four winds blow Your justice,
Come and harvest of the earth;
Turn our mourning into dancing
As we herald Your return.

1550 Johnny Parks
Copyright © 2001 Thankyou Music

THERE'S A NEW SONG UPON MY LIPS,
A song I always knew.
Thank You for all that You do.
There is fire burning in my heart,
A fire of faith in You.
I believe all the things we can do.

> *You're the God of great things,*
> *You're the God of great things.*
> *I won't hold back my thanks to You.*
> *Thank You, thank You,*
> *Hey, Jesus, I adore You.*
> *Thank You, thank You,*
> *Hey, Jesus, I live for You.*

There's a beat pounding through my feet,
A new dance of thanks to You.
I'm tasting the joy found in You.
There is courage building in my heart;
A strength that comes from You.
I'm going to live my life for You.

1551 David Fellingham
Copyright © 1999 Thankyou Music

THERE'S A PAGEANT OF TRIUMPH IN GLORY,
As Jesus the King takes His throne.
The shame of the cross is exchanged for a
crown,
And heaven applauds the King.
The Son has the Father's approval,
He perfectly followed the plan
To suffer and die for the sins of the world,
He poured out His love for our shame.

> *Let God arise with shouts of joy,*
> *With songs of praise and trumpet sound;*
> *Let music play and hearts be free,*
> *Let God arise!*

Death could not keep Him in prison,
He burst through the shackles of hell;
He settled the score with the evil one,
And heaven applauds the King.
The fullness of Christ is my treasure,
I've cast off the past with its shame.
The power of the Father has raised me to life,
I'm a son, I'm forgiven and free.

1552 Terry Virgo & Stuart Townend
Copyright © 2000 Thankyou Music

THERE'S A PEOPLE
God has chosen from the nations,
He has ransomed from the prisons
For His joy, for His delight.
He has known them
From before He made the heavens,
And His love has spanned the ages,
How He longs to bring them home!

> *Oh, that we might see Your glory, Lord.*
> *(Men)*
> *Oh, that we might see Your face. (Women)*
> *Oh, that we might be with You forever.*
> *(Men)*
> *Oh, that we might be with You. (Women)*
> *Knowing You as You have known us, (All)*
> *Faith eclipsed by what we see:*
> *One with You for all eternity!*

We're that people
You have rescued from our blindness,
You have come to live within us,
To share Your peace, to share Your joy.
Come and fill us,
Flood our spirits with Your fullness,
Let us taste the wine of heaven,
Only You can satisfy.

1553 James Taylor
Copyright © 2000 Thankyou Music

THERE'S NO LOVE GREATER THAN
YOUR LOVE,
There's no love greater than You.
There's no love greater than Your love,
There's no love greater than You.

I want to hear it sung around the world
That Jesus, You are Lord of all.
And our praises ring that You are King
Of all the heavens and the earth.
And at Your name we bow,
You've turned our mourning into dancing.

Want to see the day when all will know
That Jesus, You are Lord of all.
And we'll hear the songs of freedom sound
Upon the lips of young and old.
And every knee shall bow,
Let all the earth rejoice with gladness.

You came with love brighter than the day.
Who can deny the wonder of Your name?
Don't let me fall,
I was born to be with You:
There's no love like You.

1554 Vicky Beeching & Steve Mitchinson
Copyright © 1999 Vineyard Songs (UK/Eire)/
Adm. by CopyCare

THERE'S NO ONE LIKE OUR GOD,
No one at all.
He gave His Son for us,
Jesus the Lord.
And who can love us like He does?
No one at all.
Oh, how we love You, Lord.

You are high above all nations,
Your glory shines above the heavens;
Humbled Yourself to love and save us:
Be praised through endless generations.

You lift the needy from the ashes,
And seat them high up with the princes.
You give the barren woman healing;
She'll dance for joy like the mother of children.

1555 Damian Lundy
Copyright © 1978 Kevin Mayhew Ltd

THE SPIRIT LIVES TO SET US FREE,
Walk, walk in the light;
He binds us all in unity,
Walk, walk in the light.

> *Walk in the light,*
> *Walk in the light,*
> *Walk in the light,*
> *Walk in the light of the Lord.*

Jesus promised life to all,
Walk, walk in the light;
The dead were wakened by His call,
Walk, walk in the light.

He died in pain on Calvary,
Walk, walk in the light;
To save the lost like you and me,
Walk, walk in the light.

We know His death was not the end,
Walk, walk in the light;
He gave His Spirit to be our friend,
Walk, walk in the light.

By Jesus' love our wounds are healed,
Walk, walk in the light;
The Father's kindness is revealed,
Walk, walk in the light.

The Spirit lives in you and me,
Walk, walk in the light;
His light will shine for all to see,
Walk, walk in the light.

1556 Dave Bilbrough
Copyright © 2000 Thankyou Music

THE VOICE OF GOD is calling
With words that roar and rage;
The passion of the Father's heart
Resounds through every age.
Multitudes are waiting
For this gospel we proclaim;
Christ Jesus came among us
That all men might be saved.

> *Show Your glory, show Your glory,*
> *Show Your glory over all the earth.*
> *Show Your glory, show Your glory,*
> *Show Your glory over all the earth.*

This is our commission,
To fill the air with praise
And to tell the people of this world
The glory of His name.
With thousands upon thousands
From every tribe and tongue
We cry, 'Worthy is the Lamb once slain,
For He has overcome!'

With tears of intercession,
Through the prayers of all the saints,
We long to reach the nations
With humility and grace.
Come touch this generation
And use us, Lord, we pray;
Fill our hearts with boldness
To do the things You say.

1557 Stuart Townend & Gary Sadler
Copyright © 2002 Thankyou Music &
Paintbrush Music

THE WONDER OF FORGIVENESS,
The comfort of Your love,
The all-surpassing pleasure
To be a friend of God.
Your thoughts to me are endless,
This joy will never end.

All I want to say is 'I love You',
All I want to give is my heart.
All I want to do is be near You,
And to walk in Your ways.
Resting in the peace of Your promise,
Trusting in the cross that You bore,
Looking for the day when I see You,
Lord, I thank You for Your faithfulness to
me.

I'm laying down my treasures
To claim the perfect prize.
I'm pulling back the curtain
To look into Your eyes.
You know my inhibitions,
But You can meet me here.

1558 Don Wallace
Copyright © 1999 PDI Worship/
Adm. by CopyCare

THE WONDER OF YOUR MERCY, Lord,
The beauty of Your grace,
That You would even pardon me
And bring me to this place.
I stand before Your holiness,
I can only stand amazed:
The sinless Saviour died to make
A covenant of grace.

I only want to serve You,
Bring honour to Your name,
And though I've often failed You,
Your faithfulness remains.
I'll glory in my weakness,
That I might know Your strength.
I will live my life at the cross of Christ,
And raise a banner to proclaim:

You welcome us before You,
Into this holy place;
The brilliance of Your glory
Demands our endless praise.
The One, the only Saviour
Has opened heaven's doors;
We can enter in, free from all our sin,
By Your cleansing sacrifice.

1559 Graham Kendrick
Copyright © 1988 Make Way Music

THIS CHILD, secretly comes in the night,
O this Child, hiding a heavenly light,
O this Child, coming to us like a stranger,
This heavenly Child.

This Child, heaven come down now
To be with us here,
Heavenly love and mercy appear,
Softly in awe and wonder come near—
To this heavenly Child.

This Child, rising on us like the sun,
O this Child, given to light everyone,
O this Child, guiding our feet on the pathway
To peace on earth.

This Child, raising the humble and poor,
O this Child, making the proud ones to fall;
O this Child, filling the hungry with good
things,
This heavenly Child.

1560 Kristyn Lennox & Keith Getty
Copyright © 2002 Thankyou Music

THIS IS LOVE, not that we loved Him,
But that He first loved us.
Left behind glories of heaven;
Took on the shame of the cross.
But in the place where love was poured
Death could not hold our risen Lord.

On Christ our solid ground,
Our hope for life is found;
The joy of our salvation.
On Christ our solid ground,
Our hope for life is found.
There is no condemnation.
There is no condemnation.

This is peace, not as the world gives,
But the true peace of Christ.
You have claimed our hearts for heaven;
Living by faith, not by sight.
Strengthen our faith in You alone
Until we stand before Your throne.

1561
Reuben Morgan
Copyright © 1995 Reuben Morgan/
Hillsong Publishing/Kingsway Music

THIS IS MY DESIRE, to honour You:
Lord, with all my heart I worship You.
All I have within me, I give You praise:
All that I adore is in You.

Lord, I give You my heart,
I give You my soul;
I live for You alone.
Every breath that I take,
Every moment I'm awake,
Lord, have Your way in me.

1562
Marie Barnett
Copyright © 1995 Mercy/Vineyard Publishing/
Adm. by CopyCare

THIS IS THE AIR I BREATHE,
This is the air I breathe:
Your holy presence living in me.
This is my daily bread,
This is my daily bread:
Your very word spoken to me.

And I, I'm desperate for You.
And I, I'm lost without You.

1563
Ian White
Copyright © 1997 Thankyou Music

THIS IS THE BEST PLACE,
This is the right place,
And we have confidence now to enter:
Let us draw near now,
With hearts sincere now,
In full assurance,
To worship Jesus.

We're worshipping the living God! (×4)

Let us consider,
For one another,
The way to love more,
As the day approaches.
Let us draw near now,
With hearts sincere now;
Let's meet together
To worship Jesus.

1564
Matt Redman
Copyright © 1995 Thankyou Music

THIS MEANS I LOVE YOU,
Singing this song;
Lord, I don't have the words,
But I do have the will.
And this means I love You,
That I take up the cross,
I will sing as I walk out this love.

Jesus, this life is for You,
Everything, Lord, that I do;
Deeds that are pleasing
And ways that are pure,
Lord, may my life bear this fruit.

For these are the plans of my heart,
Yet often I'm missing the mark;
See my desire to live in Your truth,
This surely means I love You.

1565
Graham Kendrick
Copyright © 2001 Make Way Music

THOUGH TRIALS WILL COME,
Don't fear, don't run.
Lift up your eyes,
Hold fast, be strong.
Have faith, keep on believing.
Lift up your eyes
For God is at work in us,
Moulding and shaping us
Out of His love for us,
Making us more like Jesus.

Consider it joy, pure joy
When troubles come.
Many trials will make you strong.
Consider it joy, pure joy
And stand your ground,
Then at last you'll wear a crown.

Though trials will come,
Won't fear, won't run.
We'll lift up our eyes,
Hold fast, be strong.
Have faith, keep on believing.
We'll lift up our eyes
For God is at work in us,
Moulding and shaping us
Out of His love for us,
Making us more like Jesus.

Joy, pure joy,
Consider it joy, pure joy.
Joy, pure joy,
Consider it joy, pure joy.

Patiently trusting Him,
Ready for anything,
Till we're complete in Him,
In everything more like Jesus.

1566 N. Tate (1652–1715) & N. Brady (1659–1726)
New Version, 1696 based on Psalm 34

THROUGH ALL THE CHANGING SCENES OF LIFE,
In trouble and in joy,
The praises of my God shall still
My heart and tongue employ.

Of His deliverance I will boast,
Till all that are distressed
From my example comfort take,
And charm their griefs to rest.

O magnify the Lord with me,
With me exalt His name;
When in distress to Him I called,
He to my rescue came.

The hosts of God encamp around
The dwellings of the just;
Deliverance He affords to all
Who on His succour trust.

O make but trial of His love;
Experience will decide
How blest are they, and only they,
Who in His truth confide.

Fear Him, ye saints, and you will then
Have nothing else to fear;
Make you His service your delight;
Your wants shall be His care.

1567 Graham Kendrick
Copyright © 1998 Make Way Music

THROUGH DAYS OF RAGE AND WONDER
We pursue the end of time,
To seize the day eternal,
The reign of love divine.

Fixing our eyes on Jesus,
We will press on day by day.
This world's vain passing pleasures
Are not our destiny.

Our ancient rites of passage
Still are the bread and wine:
Our hope a cross that towers
Over the wrecks of time.

Through days of rage and wonder,
By the awesome power of prayer
God will shake every nation,
Secrets will be laid bare.
And if His light increasing
Casts deeper shadows here,
Safe in His holy presence,
Love will cast out our fear.

Through days of rage and wonder,
You will give us strength to stand
And seek a heavenly city
Not built by human hands.
Now is the only moment
Within our power to change:
To give back in obedience
While life and breath remain.

1568 Matt Redman
Copyright © 2000 Thankyou Music

TIME IS TOO SHORT to say it's okay,
To think I can live this way
For just another day.
So I'll search through the night
For the One my heart loves,
Won't stop till I've found You,
For Lord, I need to hold You close.

Be the King of this heart again,
Be the Lord of this life.
In my soul there's a cry today:
Be the King of this heart,
Be the King of this heart.

I've stood in the desert and thirsted for You,
I've run through the city, now I won't let go:
I'm throwing myself on Your mercy, O God,
You say: 'It's all or nothing.'
I'm saying: 'Jesus have it all.'

Be the light for my eyes,
Be the strength for my feet,
Be the love of my soul,
Be my everything.
Be my day and my night,
When I wake, when I sleep,
Undivided my heart will be.

1569 James E. Seddon (1915–83)
Copyright © Mrs M. Seddon/Jubilate Hymns Ltd

TO HIM WE COME –
Jesus Christ our Lord,
God's own living Word,
His dear Son:
In Him there is no east and west,
In Him all nations shall be blest;
To all He offers peace and rest –
Loving Lord!

In Him we live –
Christ our strength and stay,
Life and Truth and Way,
Friend divine:
His power can break the chains of sin,
Still all life's storms without, within,
Help us the daily fight to win –
Living Lord!

For Him we go –
Soldiers of the cross,
Counting all things loss,
Him to know;
Going to every land and race,
Preaching to all redeeming grace,
Building His church in every place –
Conquering Lord!

With Him we serve –
His the work we share
With saints everywhere,
Near and far;
One in the task that faith requires,
One in the zeal that never tires,
One in the hope His love inspires –
Coming Lord!

Onward we go –
Faithful, bold and true,
Called His will to do
Day by day
Till, at the last, with joy we'll see
Jesus in glorious majesty;
Live with Him through eternity –
Reigning Lord!

1570 Matthew Bridle
Copyright © 1998 Thankyou Music

TO WALK WITH YOU, to know You near me,
To know Your voice, to hear You call me;
This is all I ask of You.
To be Your son, to feel You hold me,
To know Your grace, to know You love me;
This is all I ask of You,
This is all I ask of You.

To be Your joy, to give You glory;
To live with You, forever with me.
To love You, Lord, as You have loved me,
Is all I ask of You,
All I ask of You.

To love Your ways, to see Your beauty,
To seek Your face with all that's in me;
This is all I ask of You.
To worship You, to be Yours only,
To cry Your name, my Lord Almighty;
This is all I ask of You,
This is all I ask of You.

To live Your life, to serve You justly,
To tell Your word, to show Your mercy;
This is all I ask of You.
To bring Your light to those who know me,
To be like You, as You are holy;
This is all I ask of You,
This is all I ask of You.

1571 Nathan Fellingham
Copyright © 2002 Thankyou Music

TO YOU, KING JESUS, we sing our song,
The First and the Last, the living One.
With eyes like fire, and feet like bronze,
Your face shines brighter than the sun,
All creation speaks Your name.

Jesus, Son of God,
You stand in all authority,
And at Your name darkness flees.
Oh, Jesus, living Word,
Reigning at the Father's right hand,
And You're clothed with majesty and
power.

To You, King Jesus, we give our hearts,
For You have come to us with Your great
  love.
You suffered death, went to the grave,
But now You're crowned with glory.
All Your people speak Your name.

And we now stand at Your side,
A people chosen as Your bride.
You've filled us with the Spirit's power,
This is the hour.
So in Your strength I'll run this race,
Covered by Your daily grace,
Pressing on to win the prize,
Till the day that You return,
And every tribe and every tongue will sing:

1572 Graham Kendrick
Copyright © 1997 Make Way Music

TO YOU, O LORD, I lift up my soul,
In You I trust, O my God.
Do not let me be put to shame,
Nor let my enemies triumph over me.

No one whose hope is in You
Will ever be put to shame;
That's why my eyes are on You, O Lord.
Surround me, defend me,
O, how I need You.
To You I lift up my soul,
To You I lift up my soul.

Show me Your ways and teach me Your
  paths,
Guide me in truth, lead me on;
For You're my God, You are my Saviour,
My hope is in You each moment of the day.

Remember, Lord, Your mercy and love
That ever flow from of old.
Remember not the sins of my youth
Or my rebellious ways.
According to Your love, remember me,
According to Your love,
For You are good, O Lord.

1573 Taizé, music: Jacques Berthier (1923–94)
Copyright © 1980 Ateliers et Presses de Taizé

UBI CARITAS et amor,
Ubi caritas Deus ibi est.

Living charity and steadfast love,
Living charity shows the heart of God.

1574 Latin, 15th Century
Tr. Percy Dearmer (1867–1936)
Copyright © Oxford University Press

UNTO US A BOY IS BORN!
King of all creation,
Came He to a world forlorn,
The Lord of every nation,
The Lord of every nation.

Cradled in a stall was He
With sleepy cows and asses;
But the very beasts could see
That He all men surpasses,
That He all men surpasses.

Herod then with fear was filled:
'A Prince,' he said, 'in Jewry!'
All the little boys he killed
At Bethlem in his fury,
At Bethlem in his fury.

Now may Mary's Son who came
So long ago to love us,
Lead us all with hearts aflame
Unto the joys above us,
Unto the joys above us.

Alpha and Omega He!
Let the organ thunder,
While the choir with peals of glee
Doth rend the air asunder,
Doth rend the air asunder!

1575 Jacques Berthier (1923–94)
Copyright © Ateliers et Presses de Taizé

WAIT FOR THE LORD, whose day is near.
Wait for the Lord: keep watch, take heart.

1576 Brian Houston
Copyright © 1999 Thankyou Music

**WE ARE CALLED TO BE PROPHETS TO THIS
NATION,**
To be the word of God in every situation;
Change my heart, change my heart today.
Who'll be the salt if the salt should lose its
  flavour?
Who'll be the salt if the salt should lose its
  flavour?
Change my heart, change my heart today.

Lord, loose the chains of oppression;
Lord, set the captives free.
Lord, fill my heart with compassion:
Shine Your light, shine Your light,
Shine Your light through me.

  Work a miracle in my heart,
  Work a miracle in my heart,
  Work a miracle in my heart,
  O Lord, today.

Lord, take all of my lies and take all of my
  greed;
Let me be a sacrifice for those who are in need
Change my heart, change my heart today.
Lord, without Your power it's all just good
  intentions;
Lord, without Your grace who could find
  redemption?
Change my heart, change my heart today.

1577 Stuart Townend
Copyright © 2002 Thankyou Music

WE ARE HEIRS OF GOD ALMIGHTY,
Apple of the Father's eye;
Free, forgiven, loved, accepted,
Clothed in righteousness divine.
Chosen to be pure and blameless
From before the world began;
Grace for every situation,
Sheltered in the Father's hand.

We have Christ at work within us,
Shaping us to be like Him;
Resurrection power sustaining
Freedom from the snares of sin.
Saying no to flesh desires,
Saying yes to righteous ways;
Filled with passion and with power,
Lights that burn in darkened days.

We've the Spirit without measure,
Helper, Comforter and Guide;
One who brings the gifts of heaven,
One who comes to walk beside.
Taste of heaven's endless pleasure,
Guarantee of what's to come;
Causing fruit to grow in action,
Bringing glory to the Son.

1578 Lara Martin (Abundant Life Ministries,
Bradford, England)
Copyright © 2002 Thankyou Music

WE ARE JOINED BY ANGELS,
Our purpose the same:
To worship the one and only God,
A little piece of heaven is in this place.

> *And we cry together: Holy, holy*
> *For there is no other like You, Lord.*
> *We declare together: You are awesome,*
> *You are to be feared, honoured and revered,*
> *For You are the Lord.*

We are joined by angels,
With one voice we sing,
As we lift our hands to honour You,
In worship, the angels extend their wings.

1579 Charlie Hall
Copyright © 2000 worshiptogether.com songs/
Six Steps Music/Adm. by Kingsway Music

WE BOW OUR HEARTS,
We bend our knees;
O Spirit, come make us humble.
We turn our eyes from evil things;
O Lord, we cast down our idols.

Give us clean hands,
Give us pure hearts;
Let us not lift our souls to another.
(Repeat)

> *O God, let us be*
> *A generation that seeks,*
> *That seeks Your face,*
> *O God of Jacob.*
> (Repeat)

1580 Kate Simmonds & Mark Edwards
Copyright © 2002 Thankyou Music

WE COME IN YOUR NAME,
For all things You have made,
And by Your word all things You sustain.
The Lamb that was slain
For our sins lives to reign,
The Lord of all, Name above all names.

We have been saved by faith
Into Your glorious name,
And this is a gift of God, freely given us.
Now all our sins are gone,
Defeated at the cross,
And we now live in You,
Raised with You by the power of God.

> *You have been lifted to the highest place,*
> *And You now live and rule forever.*
> *We come to bring You the highest praise,*
> *For You are King of kings forever:*
> *Son of God, Jesus!*

Holy is the Lamb,
Worthy of glory, worthy of honour.
High and lifted up,
And seated in majesty,
Your throne will last forever (more).
(Repeat)

1581 Matt Redman
Copyright © 2002 Thankyou Music

WE COULD WATCH YOU FROM AFAR,
And forever be amazed
At how glorious You are.
Yet You've drawn us close to You,
Where the wonder's greater still,
And You overwhelm us, God.

> *And we rejoice with trembling in our*
> *   hearts,*
> *Bring You a song of reverence and love.*
> *Jesus, how good, how great You are,*
> *And we rejoice with trembling*
> *Before Your throne.*

Who could fully voice the praise
Of the God of endless days,
Tell a fraction of Your worth?
For we only sing in part
Of the grace of who You are;
Just an echo, just a glimpse.

1582 Chris Tomlin
Copyright © 1998 worshiptogether.com songs/
Adm. by Kingsway Music

WE FALL DOWN, we lay our crowns
At the feet of Jesus.
The greatness of mercy and love,
At the feet of Jesus.

And we cry holy, holy, holy.
And we cry holy, holy, holy.
And we cry holy, holy, holy
Is the Lamb.

1583 Edward J. Burns
Copyright © Edward J. Burns

WE HAVE A GOSPEL TO PROCLAIM,
Good news for all throughout the earth;
The gospel of a Saviour's name:
We sing His glory, tell His worth.

Tell of His birth at Bethlehem,
Not in a royal house or hall
But in a stable dark and dim:
The Word made flesh, a light for all.

Tell of His death at Calvary,
Hated by those He came to save;
In lonely suffering on the cross
For all He loved His life He gave.

Tell of that glorious Easter morn:
Empty the tomb, for He was free.
He broke the power of death and hell
That we might share His victory.

Tell of His reign at God's right hand,
By all creation glorified;
He sends His Spirit on His Church
To live for Him, the Lamb who died.

Now we rejoice to name Him King:
Jesus is Lord of all the earth.
This gospel message we proclaim:
We sing His glory, tell His worth.

1584 Doug Horley
Copyright © 1999 Thankyou Music

WE HAVE THIS TREASURE IN JARS OF CLAY.
For all our frailty, You have entrusted us
To shine Your goodness
And life throughout the nations.
We may be pressed hard from every side,
But we will not be crushed,
Your hope will strengthen us.
And when the hard times squeeze so tight,
May they release more
Of the fragrance of Jesus.

And let Your glory shine,
O let Your glory shine.
O let Your glory shine
Through our lives, by Your grace,
May we overflow with Jesus.

May we shine like, may we shine like,
May we shine like stars in the darkness.
May we shine like, may we shine like,
May we shine like stars.

1585 Ken Riley
Copyright © 2001 Thankyou Music

WELL, I CALL UPON MY FATHER
In the name of Christ Your Son,
Let the streams of Your forgiveness
Come upon me as a flood.

I give my love to my Creator,
Reveal my heart unto my God.
I bring my life before the Healer,
For I know in You my shame
Will be thrown down.

For with sin there's separation,
Yet by grace through faith I'm saved;
Can You hear my spirit crying,
'Come and wash my sin away'?

You're washing me down,
You're washing me down.
(Repeat)

Well, I call upon my Father
In the name of Christ Your Son,
Now I've tasted Your forgiveness,
My redemption through Your blood.

1586 Alan Rose
Copyright © 2000 Thankyou Music

WE LOOK TO YOU, ALMIGHTY GOD,
You are high and lifted up,
You are sovereign over all
That You have made.
Over kingdoms and their kings,
You are Lord of everything,
Over things on earth
And things that are unseen.

And we rejoice in You,
We put our trust in You,
And with one voice we give You praise.
Singing, let Your kingdom come,
And let Your will be done,
And through Your people
Make Your glory known.

Lord, we come to seek Your face,
Let Your glory fill this place,
We are hungry for Your
Presence in this hour.
To behold You as You are,
Heaven's bright and morning Star,
Let our hearts be changed,
And let Your kingdom come!

1587 Matt Redman
Copyright © 1998 Thankyou Music

WE'RE GONNA SING LIKE THE SAVED.
We're gonna sing like the saved.
We're gonna sing like the saved.
We're gonna sing like the saved.

It is our duty and our joy,
In every time and every place,
Your gates we'll enter to give thanks,
Your courts we'll run into with praise.

A joyful noise we will make (×4)

You put Your joy in our hearts (×4)

We're gonna dance like the saved (×4)

1588 Stuart Townend
Copyright © 1998 Thankyou Music

WE'RE LONGING FOR YOUR PRESENCE,
(Men – women echo)
We're waiting on Your promise,
That You will flood the nation
With mercy and with justice.
We've tasted of Your goodness,
We've waded in Your river,
Yet still the streets are deserts,
And men cry out in hunger.
Let sinners find forgiveness,
The lonely find a family;
'Cause lips that mock and curse You
To sing of Your salvation.

(All)
Open the heavens and come down.
Come in Your glory and Your power.
Send Your revival rain:
Replenish this land again!
Open the heavens and come down,
Come down!

We want a way of living *(Men – women echo)*
That ushers in Your kingdom:
Faith, purity and passion,
And love without condition.
Come shake the ground on which we stand,
Till all we need is found in You;
Then pour the fire into our hearts
To do the work that You would do.

(All)
Open the heavens and come down.
Come in Your glory and Your power.
Send Your revival rain:
Replenish this heart again!
Open the heavens and come down,
Come down!

1589 American Folk Hymn

WERE YOU THERE when they crucified my Lord?
Were you there when they crucified my Lord?
Oh, sometimes it causes me to tremble,
tremble, tremble.
Were you there when they crucified my Lord?

Were you there when they nailed Him to the tree?
Were you there when they nailed Him to the tree?
Oh, sometimes it causes me to tremble,
tremble, tremble.
Were you there when they nailed Him to the tree?

Were you there when they laid Him in the tomb?
Were you there when they laid Him in the tomb?
Oh, sometimes it causes me to tremble,
tremble, tremble.
Were you there when they laid Him in the tomb?

Were you there when God raised Him from the dead?
Were you there when God raised Him from the dead?
Oh, sometimes it causes me to tremble,
tremble, tremble.
Were you there when God raised Him from the dead?

1590 Robin Mark
Copyright © 2000 Integrity's Hosanna! Music/
Sovereign Music UK

WE SEE THE LORD,
And He is high upon the throne,
And His glory fills the heavens and the earth.
One like a Lamb
Who was slain is on the throne,
And so I cast my crown before You
And bow down to praise.

For everything cries holy.
Oh, everything cries holy.
Oh, everything cries holy to You, Lord.
(Repeat)

1591 Kate Simmonds & Stuart Townend
Copyright © 2001 Thankyou Music

WE'VE COME TO PRAISE YOU,
'Cause You're worthy.
Nobody like You in Your glory.
We love to praise You,
'Cause You're holy, awesome,
Wonderful, mighty God.

And everything that You do
Comes from a heart of love
And a hand of mercy;
For You are faithful and true,
Working all things for good
For those who love You.

For if God in love did not spare His Son,
But He gave Him up for His chosen ones,
How much more will He freely give to us
Who call upon His name? *(×4)*

1592 Reuben Morgan
Copyright © 1997 Reuben Morgan/
Hillsong Publishing/Kingsway Music

WE WILL SEEK YOUR FACE, Almighty God,
Turn and pray for You to heal our land.
Father, let revival start in us,
Then every heart will know Your kingdom
   come.

   Lifting up the name of the Lord
   In power and in unity,
   We will see the nations turn,
   Touching heaven, changing earth,
   Touching heaven, changing earth.

Never looking back, we'll run the race;
Giving You our lives, we'll gain the prize.
We will take the harvest given us,
Though we sow in tears, we'll reap in joy.

Send revival, send revival,
Send revival to us.
(Repeat)

1593 Lara Martin (Abundant Life Ministries,
Bradford, England)
Copyright © 2002 Thankyou Music

WHAT A DAY TO BE ALIVE,
What a time to live my life,
To have a destiny and call,
And see it day by day unfold.
What a day to know You, Lord,
To live and walk within Your love,
To see the wondrous things You've done,
And know there's greater things to come.

And we sense the wonder of it all,
We feel the urgency;
There's not a day to be wasted.
God, help Your church, help us to see.

   This is our time, this is our day;
   Now's not the time to hold back or delay.
   Dreams can live again,
   Faith and hope restored.
   Taste and see that the Lord is good;
   This is the day of salvation,
   A time to break free from containment.
   People need, people need the Lord.

1594 Neil Bennetts
Copyright © 2001 Thankyou Music

WHAT CAN I SAY but 'I love You'?
What can I say but 'I praise You'?
As the train of Your robe fills this temple,
As the sound of Your voice fills this place.
What can I do but to bow down?
What can I do but to worship?
Only You are the One who is worthy,
Only You are the One who is Lord.

Great is the Lord, so great is the Lord,
Righteous and true God, holy and pure.
I fall on my knees confessing my need
For more of Your presence, Lord.

1595 William Chatterton Dix (1837–98)

WHAT CHILD IS THIS, who, laid to rest
On Mary's lap is sleeping:
Whom angels greet with anthems sweet,
While shepherds watch are keeping?
This, this is Christ the King,
Whom shepherds guard and angels sing:
Haste, haste, to bring Him praise,
The babe, the Son of Mary.

Why lies He in such mean estate,
Where ox and ass are feeding?
Good Christians, fear, for sinners here
The silent Word is pleading.
Nails, spear shall pierce Him through,
The cross be borne for me, for you.
Hail, hail the Word made flesh,
The babe, the Son of Mary.

So bring Him incense, gold and myrrh,
Come, peasant, king, to own Him;
The King of kings salvation brings,
Let loving hearts enthrone Him.
Raise, raise a song on high,
The virgin sings her lullaby.
Joy, joy for Christ is born,
The babe, the Son of Mary.

1596 Dave Bilbrough
Copyright © 1999 Thankyou Music

WHAT LOVE IS THIS,
That took my place?
Instead of wrath,
You poured Your grace on me.
What can I do
But simply come
And worship You?

I surrender, I surrender,
I surrender all to You.

What love is this
That comes to save?
Upon the cross
You bore my guilt and shame.
To You alone
I give my heart
And worship You.

A greater love
No man has seen;
It breaks sin's power
And sets the prisoner free.
With all I have
And all I am,
I worship You.

1597 Doug Horley & Steve Whitehouse
Copyright © 2001 Thankyou Music

WHAT LOVE IS THIS? The love of Jesus,
That gave its all, that cost His life.
Flesh torn by nails, life cruelly taken,
The Father's Son, love's sacrifice.

And I thank You, Lord, for loving me,
And I lift my hands so gratefully.
And I thank You, Lord, that I can be
A child of Yours eternally.

You are my King, You are my Saviour,
You'll always be a friend to me.
Safe in Your arms now and forever
Your love shines bright, my morning star.

Now let Your power rain down upon me;
Such peace and joy cascading down.
May Your love touch all those around me;
I'll shine for You, I'll shine for You.

1598 Joel Houston
Copyright © 1999 Joel Houston/
Hillsong Publishing/Kingsway Music

WHAT TO SAY, LORD?
It's You who gave me life,
And I can't explain just how much You mean
   to me
Now that You have saved me, Lord.
I give all that I am to You,
That every day I can be a light that shines
   Your name.

Every day, Lord,
I'll learn to stand upon Your word,
And I pray that I,
That I may come to know You more,
That You would guide me
In every single step I take,
That every day I can be Your light unto the
   world.

Every day, it's You I'll live for,
Every day, I'll follow after You.
Every day, I'll walk with You, my Lord.

It's You I live for every day,
It's You I live for every day,
It's You I live for every day.

1599 Bob Kauflin
Copyright © 2000 PDI Praise/Adm. by CopyCare

WHAT WISDOM ONCE DEVISED THE PLAN
Where all our sin and pride
Was placed upon the perfect Lamb
Who suffered, bled and died?
The wisdom of a sovereign God
Whose greatness will be shown,
When those who crucified Your Son
Rejoice around Your throne.

And oh, the glory of the cross,
That You would send Your Son for us.
I gladly count my life as loss
That I might come to know
The glory of, the glory of the cross.

What righteousness was there revealed
That sets the guilty free,
That justifies ungodly men
And calls the filthy clean?
A righteousness that proved to all
Your justice has been met,
And holy wrath is satisfied
Through one atoning death.

What mercy now has been proclaimed
For those who would believe?
A love incomprehensible,
Our minds could not conceive.
A mercy that forgives my sin
And makes me like Your Son.
And now I'm loved forevermore,
Because of what You've done.

1600 Stuart Townend
Copyright © 2002 Thankyou Music

WHAT WONDER OF GRACE is this,
What story of passion divine,
Where judgement and mercy kiss,
Where power and love are entwined?
No tongue can speak this glory,
No words express the joy You bring
As I enter the courts of the King.

My desire is to come to this place,
My desire is to look on Your face,
Perfect in beauty, in truth and love,
Your glory shines over all the earth;
The King who lavishes grace on us is here.

Your will is my daily bread,
Enough for my plenty and need;
I'll live by the words You've said,
And follow wherever You lead.
And though my flesh may fail me,
You prove Your grace in all I do,
Lord, my heart is devoted to You.

1601 Jan Struther (1901–53)
Copyright © Oxford University Press

WHEN A KNIGHT WON HIS SPURS in the
    stories of old,
He was gentle and brave, he was gallant and
    bold;
With a shield on his arm and a lance in his
    hand,
For God and for valour he rode through the
    land.

No charger have I, and no sword by my side,
Yet still to adventure and battle I ride,
Though back into storyland giants have fled,
And the knights are no more and the dragons
    are dead.

Let faith be my shield and let joy be my steed
'Gainst the dragons of anger, the ogres of
    greed;
And let me set free, with the sword of my
    youth,
From the castle of darkness, the power of the
    truth.

1602 Paul Oakley
Copyright © 1998 Thankyou Music

WHEN DEEP CALLS TO DEEP
There's a stirring inside of me,
A feeling that words won't describe;
Like I'm hearing Your song
Touching my spirit,
Calling me deeper with You.

And the thirst in my soul
Just to meet with You, God,
I'm feeling the pull of Your love;
Like the crash of Your waves,
Like the roar or Your waterfalls,
Drawing me on into You.

And all I know is it's You.
And I cry out to You.

Give me oil for my wounds,
Give me wine for my heart,
Give me strength for today,
And I will stand.
Give me salve for my eyes,
Give me truth for the lies,
Give me love in my life
And I will run with You.

1603 Drew Land
Copyright © 2000 Thankyou Music

WHEN I COME FACE TO FACE
With the One the angels praise,
I'm in awe, I'm amazed
With a God full of grace.
It's the love You have shown
That allows me at Your throne
To adore, and how I do:
Father, I'm in love with You.

Here I am with lifted hands,
I give You praise
And I exalt Your holy name
With all I have,
With all the strength that I can raise.
And here I am once again,
I lift my voice
With all the angels 'round Your throne.
I adore and I worship You alone.

I am in love,
I am in love with all my heart,
With all my soul, and all my mind
With all the strength I've ever known.
I am in love,
I am in love with the King
And with His Son, the One who loved
With His life and with His blood.

1604

WHEN I NEEDED A NEIGHBOUR,
Were you there, were you there?
When I needed a neighbour, were you there?

And the creed and the colour
And the name won't matter,
Were you there?

I was hungry and thirsty,
Were you there, were you there?
I was hungry and thirsty, were you there?

I was cold, I was naked,
Were you there, were you there?
I was cold, I was naked, were you there?

When I needed a shelter,
Were you there, were you there?
When I needed a shelter, were you there?

When I needed a healer,
Were you there, were you there?
When I needed a healer, were you there?

Wherever you travel,
I'll be there, I'll be there.
Wherever you travel, I'll be there.

And the creed and the colour
And the name won't matter,
I'll be there.

1605

WHEN I SING MY PRAISE to You,
I am lifted up to higher ground.
Something happens in my soul
When I lift my voice to worship You.
Feels like sunshine on my face,
A cool breeze in a desert place.

When I worship You,
Heaven comes to me,
Heaven comes to me.
When I worship You,
Heaven comes to me,
Heaven comes to me.

Heaven is where I belong,
Where the angels sing before Your throne.
I am caught up in their sound,
When I lift my voice to worship You.
From beyond where eyes can see,
Love is pouring over me.

I will worship You,
Heaven come to me,
Heaven come to me.
I will worship You,
Heaven come to me,
Heaven come to me.

1606

WHEN I SURVEY the wondrous cross
On which the Prince of Glory died,
My richest gain I count but loss,
And pour contempt on all my pride.

See from His head, His hands, His feet,
Sorrow and love flow mingled down;
Did e'er such love and sorrow meet
Or thorns compose so rich a crown?

Oh, the wonderful cross,
Oh, the wonderful cross
Bids me come and die and find
That I may truly live.
Oh, the wonderful cross,
Oh, the wonderful cross,
All who gather here by grace
Draw near and bless Your name.

Were the whole realm of nature mine,
That were an offering far too small.
Love so amazing, so divine
Demands my soul, my life, my all.

1607

WHEN I WAS LOST, You came and rescued
me;
Reached down into the pit and lifted me.
O Lord, such love,
I was as far from You as I could be.
You know all the things I've ever done,
But Jesus' blood has cancelled every one.
O Lord, such grace
To qualify me as Your own.

There is a new song in my mouth,
There is a deep cry in my heart,
A hymn of praise to Almighty God –
hallelujah!
And now I stand firm on this Rock,
My life is hidden now with Christ in God.
The old has gone and the new has come –
hallelujah!
Your love has lifted me.

Now I have come into Your family,
For the Son of God has died for me.
O Lord, such peace,
I am as loved by You as I could be.
In the full assurance of Your love,
Now with every confidence we come.
O Lord, such joy
To know that You delight in us.

Many are the wonders You have done,
And many are the things that You have planned.
How beautiful the grace that gives to us
All that we don't deserve,
All that we cannot earn,
But is a gift of love.

1608 Stuart Townend
Copyright © 2001 Thankyou Music

WHEN LOVE CAME DOWN to earth
And made His home with men,
The hopeless found a hope,
The sinner found a friend.
Not to the powerful
But to the poor He came,
And humble, hungry hearts
Were satisfied again.

What joy, what peace has come to us!
What hope, what help, what love!

When every unclean thought,
And every sinful deed
Was scourged upon His back
And hammered through His feet.
The Innocent is cursed,
The guilty are released;
The punishment of God
On God has brought me peace.

Come lay your heavy load
Down at the Master's feet;
Your shame will be removed,
Your joy will be complete.
Come crucify your pride,
And enter as a child;
For those who bow down low
He'll lift up to His side.

1609 Alan Rose
Copyright © 2000 Thankyou Music

WHEN MY HEART IS FAINT within me,
And my troubles multiply,
I will lift my head to see You
Seated at the Father's side.
You have triumphed over Satan,
You're the firstborn from the grave.
You are always interceding,
You are able now to save.

You are Jesus Christ, faithful One,
Risen King, Champion.
You deserve the highest praise,
The Lamb of God,
Who once was slain for our sin.

In my heart I am persuaded
As the Spirit testifies,
And with glory and rejoicing
'Abba, Father' is my cry.
You have raised me up with Jesus
And in Him I am Your son,
So I glory in Your goodness,
In the things that You have done.

1610 Matt Redman
Copyright © 2001 Thankyou Music

WHEN MY HEART RUNS DRY
And there's no song to sing,
No holy melody,
No words of love within,
I recall the height from which
This fragile heart has slipped.

And I'll remember You,
I will turn back and do
The things I used to do
For the love of You.
Lord, I'll remember You,
I will turn back and do
The things I need to do
For the love You.

You are my soul's desire,
You are the hope within,
You bring my heart to life,
You make my spirit sing.
I recall the height from which
This fragile heart has slipped.

1611 Reuben Morgan
Copyright © 1998 Reuben Morgan/
Hillsong Publishing/Kingsway Music

WHEN THE DARKNESS FILLS MY SENSES,
When my blindness keeps me from Your
  touch,
Jesus come.
When my burden keeps me doubting,
When my memories take the place of You,
Jesus come.

And I'll follow You there,
To the place where we meet,
And I'll lay down my pride
As You search me again.
Your unfailing love, Your unfailing love,
Your unfailing love over me again.

1612

WHEN THE ROAD IS ROUGH AND STEEP,
Fix your eyes upon Jesus.
He alone has power to keep,
Fix your eyes upon Him.
Jesus is a gracious friend,
One on whom you can depend,
He is faithful to the end,
Fix your eyes upon Him.

1613

WHEN WE TURN OUR HEARTS TO HEAVEN
And bow down,
We'll see fathers and the children reconciled.
We'll be the dreamers of Your dreams.
We'll be the dreamers of Your dreams.

When Your fire falls from heaven,
We will rend our hearts to You.
We will tell it to our children,
All the wonders You have done.
And in every generation
We will sing of Your great love.
When Your fire falls from heaven
We'll return to You again!
We'll be the dreamers of Your dreams.
We'll be the dreamers of Your dreams.

1614

WHEN WORDS ARE NOT ENOUGH
To tell of all You've done,
I bow the knee, let silence speak,
And gaze upon Your majesty.

These songs could not convey
A picture of Your love;
And knowing this, my life I give
To You, an offering of praise.

And I surrender all,
And I surrender all;
Unveil my heart to see
The wonder of Your worth,
As I surrender all,
As I surrender all.

The worship You require
Is brokenness of heart;
So here I stand with open hands,
Surrendered to Your love and power.

1615

WHEN YOU PRAYED BENEATH THE TREES,
It was for me, O Lord;
When You cried upon Your knees,
How could it be, O Lord?
When in blood and sweat and tears
You dismissed Your final fears,
When You faced the soldiers' spears,
You stood for me, O Lord.

When their triumph looked complete,
It was for me, O Lord;
When it seemed like Your defeat,
They could not see, O Lord!
When You faced the mob alone
You were silent as a stone,
And a tree became Your throne;
You came for me, O Lord.

When You stumbled up the road,
You walked for me, O Lord,
When You took Your deadly load,
That heavy tree, O Lord;
When they lifted You on high,
And they nailed You up to die,
And when darkness filled the sky,
It was for me, O Lord.

When You spoke with kingly power,
It was for me, O Lord,
In that dread and destined hour,
You made me free, O Lord;
Earth and heaven heard You shout,
Death and hell were put to rout,
For the grave could not hold out;
You are for me, O Lord.

1616

WHERE CAN I GO without You, Lord?
What can I do, how can I stand?
You are my comfort and my strength.
You are my shield and my right hand.

And You pour out healing on me,
Pour out healing.
And You make my spirit soar,
And You make my burden light,
And You soothe me in the storm,
And You go before me in the fight.

1617 Robin Mark
Copyright © 2000 Thankyou Music

WHERE COULD I FIND SOMEONE LIKE YOU?
Unbounded love in all You do.
So I seek to know You more,
I'll press into Your word again,
And drawing on Your Spirit's power,
And drinking from that well again.

For heaven and earth are in Your hands,
This universe within Your plans.
Dust of life no eye can see,
They only stir when You command.
Some divine permission given,
Empowered by Your mighty hand.

And You knew me in the secret place
As my being formed, You beheld my days.
And You know me now, You know all my
ways,
Nothing's hid from You,
I'm with You always.

My weakest means, my poorest words
To tell this world of Your redeeming love.
By Your Holy Spirit's power
Is articulation given,
Message to the poor in heart,
That Jesus Christ is risen again.

And You knew me in the secret place
As my being formed, You decreed my
days.
And You know me now, You know all my
ways,
Nothing's hid from You,
I'm with You always.

1618 Gareth Robinson
Copyright © 2001 Thankyou Music

WHO CAN COMPARE with You, my Father;
Loving and kind, faithful and true?
When You forgive my heart that is broken,
I gratefully sing my love to You.

I worship You,
I love You:
All that I am
Sings this song of praise.

Here I will dwell in the arms of my Father,
Knowing Your grace, hearing Your voice;
Trusting Your word, feeling Your peace,
Resting in You and in Your love.

And I abide in You,
I abide with You.

1619 Geraldine Latty & Carey Luce
Copyright © 2002 Thankyou Music

WHO CAN STAND BEFORE THE LORD
In His holy place?
Who can walk upon the hill of the Lord?
Only he whose hands are clean,
Only he whose heart is pure
Can stand before the Lord.

I will stand, I will come
Before the presence of the King:
For His blood washes me from sin,
I enter in.

There is One who stands for me
In the holy place,
And He walked the lonely hill to the cross.
And I know His hands are clean,
And I know His heart is pure,
He is Jesus Christ the Lamb.

1620 Evan Rogers
Copyright © 1998 Thankyou Music

WHO COULD OFFER US ABUNDANT LIFE?
Who could be the only way?
Who could be the purest sacrifice?
Who could have the power
To rise from the grave?

Who could be our only righteousness?
Who could be the One who saves?
Who could be the God who became flesh?
Who could have the Name above every
name?

(It's) only Jesus
Shines like the sun.
Only Jesus,
The King of kings, the Holy One.
(It's) only Jesus,
The Son of God, the Son of Man.
Only Jesus,
The Prince of Peace, the great I Am.

Who could give us living water?
Who could be the Bread of Life?
Who could overcome the darkness?
Who could be the Truth, our shining light?

Now only I can offer up my life;
There's nothing less that I could give
To Him who gave up all His heavenly rights
So that I might live.

1621

Joannah Oyeniran
Copyright © 2002 Thankyou Music

WHO IS LIKE YOU, Lord Almighty?
Crowned in splendour, robed in majesty,
Holy is Your name.
God of justice, rich in mercy.
Grace that flows from awesome glory,
The wonder of Your ways.
Mighty in power, perfect in sovereignty,
The revelation, You laid it aside for me
And bore human frame in Jesus.

So I exalt You, God of glory,
And I will worship the Lord of eternity.
King of the nations, my wonderful Saviour,
God our Creator, my heavenly Father.
I worship only You.

1622

Neil Bennetts
Copyright © 2002 Thankyou Music

WHO IS THERE LIKE THE LORD OUR GOD,
Faithful beyond all compare?
Glorious in such holiness
With power to heal and to save.

> *You shall be called the Saviour eternal,*
> *There is grace in Your heart, and Your name.*
> *And You shall be known through all*
> *generations*
> *As the hope for the life that receives.*

Let heaven rejoice, You are wonderful;
Creation sings out to Your praise.
You are the Lord, You are beautiful;
Each work of Your hand shall proclaim.

A love beyond reason, this gift of life;
The mercy of God in Your sacrifice.
The fountain of truth that can satisfy,
And it's found in You, Jesus,
And it's found in You, Jesus,
And it's found in You, Jesus.

1623

David Ruis
Copyright © 1996 Mercy/Vineyard Publishing/
Adm. by CopyCare

WHOM HAVE I BUT YOU?
Whom have I but You?

Though the mountains fall,
They fall into the sea.

Though the coloured dawn
May turn to shades of grey.

Though the questions asked
May never be resolved.

1624

J.A.P. Booth
Copyright © Paul Booth/Adm. by CopyCare

WHO PUT THE COLOURS IN THE RAINBOW?
Who put the salt into the sea?
Who put the cold into the snowflake?
Who made you and me?
Who put the hump upon the camel?
Who put the neck on the giraffe?
Who put the tail upon the monkey?
Who made hyenas laugh?
Who made whales and snails and quails?
Who made hogs and dogs and frogs?
Who made bats and rats and cats?
Who made everything?

Who put the gold into the sunshine?
Who put the sparkle in the stars?
Who put the silver in the moonlight?
Who made Earth and Mars?
Who put the scent into the roses?
Who taught the honey bee to dance?
Who put the tree inside the acorn?
It surely can't be chance!
Who made seas and leaves and trees?
Who made snow and winds that blow?
Who made streams and rivers flow?
God made all of these!

1625

Annie Spiers
Copyright © 1992 Annie Spiers

WHO'S THE KING OF THE JUNGLE?
Who's the king of the sea?
Who's the king of the universe
And who's the king of me?
I'll tell you J-E-S-U-S is,
He's the King of me,
He's the King of the universe,
The jungle and the sea.

1626

Scott Underwood
Copyright © 1999 Mercy/Vineyard Publishing/
Adm. by CopyCare

WHO'S THE ONLY LIGHT that shines and
    never fades?
The Light of the world, Jesus.
Who's the only light that drives the dark
    away?
The Light of the world, Jesus.

> *It's all about Jesus, Jesus,*
> *It's all about Jesus, Jesus.*

Who's the only Word that made all things?
The Word was God, Jesus.
He's the only truth, the fullness of the Lord,
The Son of God, Jesus.

You're the Way, the Truth and the Life.
You're the Way, the Truth and the Life.

1627

WITH A PRAYER You fed the hungry,
With a cry You stilled the storm;
With a look You had compassion
On the desperate and forlorn.
With a touch You healed the leper,
With a shout You raised the dead;
With a word expelled the demons,
With a blessing broke the bread.

Love incarnate, love divine,
Captivate this heart of mine
Till all I do speaks of You.

As a sheep before the shearer
You were silent in Your pain;
You endured humiliation
At the hands of those You'd made.
And as hell unleashed its fury
You were lifted on a tree,
Crying 'Father God, forgive them,
Place their punishment on Me.'

I will feed the poor and hungry,
I will stand up for the truth;
I will take my cross and follow
To the corners of the earth.
And I ask that You so fill me
With Your peace, Your power, Your breath,
That I never love my life so much
To shrink from facing death.

1628

WITH HIS HANDS HE MADE ME,
Breathed His life within me;
With His heart He loved me,
Yet I turned away.
In His love He sought me,
Came to earth to save me;
Punished my rebellion
With His sacrifice.

I'll come to the Giver of life,
I'll drink from His well of delights:
I'll yield to His tender embrace,
I'll be to Him an offering of praise.

Here I stand before You,
Needing Your forgiveness,
Thirsting for Your Spirit,
Longing for Your touch.
Let the flame within me
Grow into a fire,
Banish all my darkness
With Your piercing light.

I'll come to the Giver of life,
I'll drink from His well of delights:
I'll yield to His tender embrace,
I'll be to Him an offering.
I'll rest in the shade of His wings,
I'll feast on the pleasure He brings,
I'll seek Him for all of my days,
I'll be to Him an offering of praise.

1629

WITH THE CHOIR OF ANGELS SINGING,
And the realm of heavenly hosts;
As those elders humbly bow,
I'd love to come to Your throne
With a simple song.

With the living creatures speaking
Praise and praise and praise again;
With the company of heaven,
I'd love to come to Your throne
With a song of love.

Hallelujah, Jesus,
Hallelujah, hallelu.
Hallelujah, Jesus,
Pouring out my heart to You.

I would bring this praise like incense
Rising to Your throne above,
Fill the air with heart-filled songs
In harmony and melody
To the One I love.

And who can tell the adoration
That will rise up to Your throne?
Every knee that day shall bow
To the King of kings,
The Holy One, the only One.
We'll all be singing...

1630

WONDERFUL GRACE,
That gives what I don't deserve,
Pays me what Christ has earned,
Then lets me go free.
Wonderful grace,
That gives me the time to change,
Washes away the stains
That once covered me.

And all that I have
I lay at the feet
Of the wonderful Saviour
Who loves me.

Wonderful love,
That held in the face of death,
Breathed in its latest breath
Forgiveness for me.
Wonderful love,
Whose power can break every chain,
Giving us life again,
Setting us free.

1631
Ashton Gardner
Copyright © 2001 Thankyou Music

WONDERFUL REDEEMER all my life,
Thank You for the grace You have shown to me.
Nothing can compare to Your heart of love,
I have Your eyes.

Sing to the Lord our God,
Lift up His name and exalt Him.
Your holiness is immense,
And we Your people will worship
Your name forever.

Righteous and majestic King of truth,
All mankind will one day bow the knee to
  You.
May our lives reflect the heart of You, O Lord,
We will live for You.

1632
Tim Hughes
Copyright © 2002 Thankyou Music

WONDERFUL, SO WONDERFUL
Is Your unfailing love;
Your cross has spoken mercy over me.
No eye has seen, no ear has heard,
No heart could fully know
How glorious, how beautiful You are.

Beautiful One, I love You,
Beautiful One, I adore,
Beautiful One, my soul must sing.

Powerful, so powerful,
Your glory fills the skies,
Your mighty works displayed for all to see.
The beauty of Your majesty
Awakes my heart to sing
How marvellous, how wonderful You are.

You opened my eyes to Your wonders anew,
You captured my heart with this love,
'Cause nothing on earth
Is as beautiful as You.
(Repeat)

My soul, my soul must sing,
My soul, my soul must sing,
My soul, my soul must sing,
Beautiful One.

1633
Louise Fellingham
Copyright © 1999 Thankyou Music

WORSHIP THE LORD,
See the splendour of His holiness.
Give to the Lord all the glory due His name.
Come and adore,
Come and lay your hearts before Him.
With thankfulness and love,
Come and shout aloud your praise.

Declare His glory among all the nations.
Declare His majesty,
His splendour and power.
Proclaim salvation,
His goodness and mercy;
For great is the Lord and most worthy,
Worthy of praise.

We are His people, belonging to our Father,
Set apart for truth, we are chosen by God.
With confidence we come,
We are free and we're forgiven.
Blessed are the ones
Who put their hope in God.

Please come upon us now,
We want to see Your face, Lord.
Soften our hearts, take us deeper into You.
Spirit, fill our minds
With the knowledge of Your wisdom.
Come and touch our mouths,
Help us tell of all You've done.

1634
Matt Redman
Copyright © 1999 Thankyou Music

WORTHY, YOU ARE WORTHY,
Much more worthy than I've known;
I cannot imagine
Just how glorious You are.
I cannot begin to tell
How deep a love You bring;
Lord, my ears have heard of You,
But now my eyes have seen.

You're worthy, You're worthy, You're worthy,
You're worthy to be praised,
Forever and a day.
(Repeat)

Glory, I give glory
To the One who saved my soul.
You found me and You freed me
From the shame that was my own.
I cannot begin to tell
How merciful You've been;
Lord, my ears have heard of You,
Now my eyes have seen.

You're worthy...

Your glory, Your glory, Your glory,
Your glory reaches high,
So high above the heavens.

1635 Stuart Townend
Copyright © 1997 Thankyou Music

WOVEN TOGETHER within the womb,
Fearfully, wonderfully made;
You know me better than I know myself,
And still You look on with pleasure.
Where can I go from Your Spirit, Lord?
Where can I hide from Your gaze?
Ocean to ocean and shore to shore,
Your hand reaches out to guide me.

> *It's all too wonderful*
> *For me to know;*
> *It's all too marvellous*
> *For me to attain.*
> *The care You show to those*
> *Who love Your name;*
> *It's all too wonderful,*
> *It's all too wonderful for me.*

Lord, You have searched me, You know me
well,
For nothing is hidden from You;
And even before there's a word on my tongue,
You know it completely, Lord.
How precious to me are Your thoughts, O God,
How great is the depth of Your love;
I know that You've numbered the sum of my
days,
I'll rest in Your perfect wisdom.

1636 Kevin Simpson
Copyright © 2000 Thankyou Music

YES, I THANK YOU, O Lord.
Yes, I thank You, O Lord.
Looking back in my life I see
Many things You have done for me.
I thank You, O Lord.

Yes, I love You...

Yes, I praise You...

Hallelujah, hallelujah, glory to Your name.
Hallelujah, hallelujah, glory to Your name.

Oui, je te remercie, Seigneur.
Oui, je te remercie, Seigneur.
En arrière dans ma vie je vois
Toutes choses que tu as fait pour moi.
Je te remercie, Seigneur.

1637 Marilyn Baker
Copyright © 1998 Marilyn Baker Music/
Kingsway Music

YESTERDAY, TODAY AND FOREVER
You're the same,
All the promises of God
Find their 'yes' in You.
Demons flee, strongholds fall,
They must bow before Your name,
No authority, no power is higher than You.

> *Let's sing our praise to the Lord,*
> *Thank You for the great things You have*
>   *done.*
> *Let's sing with all of our hearts,*
> *There's no Father like You.*
> *Let's dance for joy to the Lord,*
> *For You have washed our sins away.*
> *We're more than conquerors,*
> *With You close by our side.*

Yesterday, today and forever
You're the same,
We need never fear
To put all our trust in You.
For Your word is a rock
And a light to show the way,
And a sword that will pierce
Through the darkness each day.

1638 Geraldine Latty
Copyright © 2001 Thankyou Music

YET WILL I PRAISE HIM,
I will lift my hands to my Creator.
Yet will I praise Him,
My Saviour and my God.
Yet will I praise Him,
I will put my trust in my Provider.
Yet will I praise Him,
Lord Jehovah, Sovereign God.

Though the fig tree doesn't blossom
And no ripened grapes appear,
Though the harvest fails
And fields provide no food;
I'll be joyful in my Saviour,
The Lord who is my strength;
He will keep my ways
And lead me in His truth.

When the night is overwhelming
And the day is far from clear,
When my heart is restless
For the peace of God;
Let Your song, Lord, through the ages,
Through the prophets You have given,
Lift my mind and heart
To gaze upon You, Lord.

Be the strength, Lord, in my weakness,
Let Your song be in my night;
Be my rock when all around is sinking sand.
Be the light, Lord, in my darkness,
Be the vision of my eyes:
In my passing days
You are the great 'I Am'.

Lord, I will praise You,
I will lift my hands to my Creator.
Lord, I will praise You,
My Saviour and my God.
Lord, I will praise You,
I will put my trust in my Provider.
Yes, I will praise You,
Lord Jehovah, Sovereign God.

1639 Gareth Robinson
Copyright © 2001 Thankyou Music

YOU ARE ALL I WANT,
You're all I need to be set free.
Your cross of death gives life to me,
Your sacrifice brings liberty.
No one else could take my place but You,
The perfect One, the holy God,
Revealed as man in Jesus Christ.
Only You could take my sin, so…

I love You, yeah, I love You, Jesus.
I love You, yeah, I love You, Jesus.

I will give to You my everything,
Abandon all my selfish dreams
To live for You and do Your will every day.
You have touched my heart
And made me whole,
You've made me clean, so I will give
My offering of love to You,
All my life lived just for You, 'cause…

1640 Reuben Morgan
Copyright © 2001 Reuben Morgan/
Hillsong Publishing/Kingsway Music

YOU ARE FOREVER IN MY LIFE,
You see me through the seasons;
Cover me with Your hand,
And lead me in Your righteousness.
And I look to You,
And I wait on You.

I'll sing to You, Lord, a hymn of love
For Your faithfulness to me.
I'm carried in everlasting arms;
You'll never let me go,
Through it all.

Hallelujah, hallelujah,
Hallelujah, hallelujah.
(Repeat)

1641 Matt & Beth Redman
Copyright © 2000 Thankyou Music

YOU ARE GOD IN HEAVEN,
And here am I on earth;
So I'll let my words be few:
Jesus, I am so in love with You.

And I'll stand in awe of You,
Yes, I'll stand in awe of You.
And I'll let my words be few:
Jesus, I am so in love with You.

The simplest of all love songs
I want to bring to You;
So I'll let my words be few:
Jesus, I am so in love with You.

1642 Reuben Morgan
Copyright © 1997 Reuben Morgan/
Hillsong Publishing/Kingsway Music

YOU ARE HOLY, holy,
Lord, there is none like You.
You are holy, holy,
Glory to You alone.

I'll sing Your praises forever,
Deeper in love with You.
Here in Your courts
Where I'm close to Your throne,
I've found where I belong.

1643 Tré Sheppard
Copyright © 2002 Thankyou Music

YOU ARE HOLY, *You are mercy,*
You are wonder, You are love.
You are faithful, You are gracious,
You are lovely, You are God.

I open my eyes so I
See Your loveliness.
I open my life so I
Know Your holiness.

If You are for us who could
Stand against us?
Surely You are with us,
Surely You are with us.

Surely You are with us,
Surely You are with us,
Surely You are with us,
Surely You are with us.

1644 Robin Mark

YOU ARE KNOWN AS THE ROCK OF AGES,
And the holy Ancient of Days.
Men of old who saw Your face, Lord,
Would not ever be the same.
When You came as God incarnate,
Walked this earth, Your glory veiled,
Those who knew You, and who loved You
Would not ever be the same.

For I have seen You, Rock of Ages,
And I will never be the same.
Oh, I love You, Rock of Ages,
And I will always love Your name.

Will You hide me, Rock of Ages,
In Your secret place of peace?
Can I feel Your burning glory?
Can I hear You when You speak?
Will You chasten me and mould me?
Will You hold me in Your will?
Oh to know You, love and serve You
And Your purposes fulfil.

1645 Neil Bennetts

YOU ARE LORD, YOU ARE LORD,
And Your glory fills this temple.
You are Lord, You are Lord,
And Your glory fills this place.
In Your presence I will honour,
As I bring my praise to You.
You are Lord, You are Lord,
And Your glory fills this place.

1646 Stuart Townend

YOU ARE MY ANCHOR,
My light and my salvation.
You are my refuge,
My heart will not fear.
Though my foes surround me on every hand,
They will stumble and fall
While in grace I stand.
In my day of trouble
You hide me and set me above
To sing this song of love.

One thing I will ask of You, this will I pray:
To dwell in Your house, O Lord, every day,
To gaze upon Your lovely face,
And rest in the Father's embrace.

Teach me Your way, Lord,
Make straight the path before me.
Do not forsake me, my hope is in You.
As I walk through life, I am confident
I will see Your goodness with every step,
And my heart directs me to seek You
In all that I do,
So I will wait for You.

1647 Mark Stevens (Abundant Life Ministries, Bradford, England)

YOU ARE MY FOUNDATION,
You are my salvation,
A very present help in times of need.
You are my protection,
You are my resurrection,
A higher place is where You're taking me.

I get lifted up on eagles' wings,
You lift me up and so I sing:

Hallelujah, hallelujah,
Hallelujah to the King.
(Repeat)

You are my Redeemer,
You are my Healer,
A promise given, one of liberty.
You are my Restorer,
You are my strong tower,
The joy of the Lord will be my strength.

1648 Mark Stevens (Abundant Life Ministries, Bradford, England)

YOU ARE MY KING, I live to know You.
Oh, to walk in the fullness of Your Spirit.
I'll abide in You and You in me,
I'll see Your desire fulfilled within me.

I am changed by You
Into Your image.
I am changed by You,
I become the same.
I am changed by You,
Like my Father God,
King of heaven.
King of heaven.

You placed in me a fire when I met You,
And the flame, it just burns brighter and
    brighter.
I'm coming after You with all that's in me,
I need You more and more each time I wake.

Glory to glory to glory, Lord,
We will never be the same.
Glory to glory to glory, Lord,
Oh, we will never, never be the same.

1649

Scott Underwood
Copyright © 1997 Mercy/Vineyard Publishing/
Adm. by CopyCare

YOU ARE MY SHEPHERD, I have no needs.
You lead me by peaceful streams,
And You refresh my life.
You hold my hand and You guide my steps,
I could walk through the valley of death,
And I won't be afraid.

Because You are in control.
You are in control.
You are in control.
You are in control.

You cause everything to work together,
You truly have a sovereign plan,
And You know who I am,
And You made who I am,
And You love who I am.

1650

Brian Houston
Copyright © 2001 Thankyou Music

YOU ARE MYSTICAL and deep.
You take Your rest, but never sleep.
You watch me like a mother does,
Every scar and every tear and fall.
You suffer long, but Your patience waits,
Your judgement always hesitates.
Your anger stays a moment,
Yet Your favour lasts a whole life long.

And I cannot stand silently
When faced with so much grace.
My chest is pounding with the need
To celebrate You, God,
And the miracle of Your love.

For You're everywhere, in every place,
In every time, in every space,
And every breath that I take You lend.
You're the only One who satisfies,
The only One who makes my life make
sense.

You are generous and kind,
So intimate and close at times,
Yet You reveal Your beauty in the twilight
And the summer evening rain.
You're in the rainbow and the dawn,
You steal my breath and then You're gone,
Yet when the morning sun breaks through,
I look for You and You are here again.

1651

Darren Clarke
Copyright © 1998 Mercy/Vineyard Publishing/
Adm. by CopyCare

YOU ARE THE FOUNTAIN OF MY LIFE
And in Your light I find my reason,
'Cause Your love reaches to the stars,
Even the great deep.
And Your love reaches to this heart
And it makes me sing.

Your love reaches me:
It's what I need, it's what I need.
Your love reaches me:
It's what I need, it's what I need.

O Lord, how priceless
Is Your unending love.
Both high and low
Find refuge in Your shadow.
(Repeat)

1652

Liz Fitzgibbon
Copyright © 2001 Moortown Music/
Kingsway Music

YOU ARE THE KING OF GLORY,
You dwell in holiness.
Your sceptre reaches for me
And I approach Your throne:

To make my prayers known to You;
Your heart of love is for me.
With boldness I draw near
To Your throne, O God,
To Your throne.

You show Your favour to me,
My faith just grows and grows.
Nothing's too hard for my God,
No prayer too hard for You.

I will make my prayers known…

1653

Chris Tomlin & Jesse Reeves
Copyright © 2002 worshiptogether.com songs/
Six Steps Music/Adm. by Kingsway Music

YOU ARE THE LORD,
The famous One, famous One;
Great is Your name in all the earth.
The heavens declare
You're glorious, glorious;
Great is Your fame beyond the earth.

And for all You've done and yet to do,
With every breath, I'm praising You.
Desire of nations and every heart,
You alone are God,
You alone are God.

The Morning Star is shining through,
And every eye is watching You.
Revealed by nature and miracles,
You are beautiful, You are beautiful.

1654 Eoghan Heaslip & Mick Goss
Copyright © 2002 Integrity's Hosanna! Music/
Sovereign Music UK/& Daybreak Music Ltd

YOU ARE THE LORD, the King of heaven
And all the earth, You'll reign forever.
First and the last, You are glorious.

Before Your throne the elders fall,
And angels sing: 'Almighty God.'
Bright Morning Star,
You are glorious, You are glorious.

To You, the nations will come,
Every tribe, every tongue
And worship before You,
The Ancient of Days,
The Name above all names,
Who is worthy of all our praise.
You are glorious.
Yeah, You are glorious.

1655 Sue Rinaldi & Caroline Bonnett
Copyright © 2001 Thankyou Music

YOU ARE THE ONE I LOVE,
You are the One that I adore.
(Repeat)

For You've called me by name,
Drawn me close to Your heart,
Washed away all my shame with Your tears.
For the rest of my days,
I will offer my life
In thanksgiving and praise to my King.

Now with You I will stay,
For Your word is my light,
And Your peace can allay all my fears;
And my victory song
Is the song of the cross,
You have won me love so divine.

Such precious, precious love.

1656 Lara Martin (Abundant Life Ministries,
Bradford, England)
Copyright © 2002 Thankyou Music

YOU ARE THE SONG THAT I SING,
A precious melody.
You are the theme of my heart.
You are my inspiration.

You are the light of my life,
How I love Your word.
It leads me closer to You.

You are my inspiration, You cause me to
sing.
You are my inspiration, the reason I live.
You are my inspiration, I'm glad I'm alive.
You are my inspiration.

Your greatness creation displays,
Such wonders to behold.
In awe I, I live my days.

How then can I be silent,
When my heart is so full?
In You I have discovered
The secret of true love,
And I want the world to know that…

1657 Brian Doerksen
Copyright © 1999 Vineyard Songs (UK/Eire)/
Adm. by CopyCare

YOU ARE THE SOVEREIGN 'I AM',
Your name is holy.
You are the pure, spotless Lamb,
Your name is holy.
You are the Almighty One,
Your name is holy.
You are the Christ, God's own Son,
Your name is holy.

In Your name
There is mercy for sin,
There is safety within,
In Your holy name.
In Your name
There is strength to remain,
To stand, in spite of pain,
In Your holy name.

1658 Tim Hughes
Copyright © 2001 Thankyou Music

YOU CALL US FIRST to love Your name,
To worship You.
To please Your heart our one desire,
O Lord.

If there's one thing we are called to do,
It's to love You, to adore You.
We will bring our all and worship You,
Bow before You, as we love You.

Your honour, Lord, Your name's renown
We long to see.
So let the glory of Your name
Be praised.

will celebrate this love,
Jesus, You are everything to me.
For what more, Lord, can I do?
I will give this heart, this life to You.

1659 Tim Hughes
Copyright © 1999 Thankyou Music

YOU CAME INTO MY LIFE,
A Saviour to my soul;
You set a hope within this heart of mine.
You said that I am Yours,
That You will never leave me.
Now I surrender all I am to You.

I will never know why You chose me, God,
But You did.
I will never know why You took that cross,
But You did, yes, You did.

While today is still today
I'll live just for Your praise,
A living sacrifice;
Holding out to be
Faithful unto You,
So in my life be glorified,
I pray.

In You, O Lord, I trust,
In You, O Lord, I live;
Do not let me stray from Your commands.
Guide me in Your way,
Protect me in Your truth,
Teach me what it means to follow You.

660 James Taylor
Copyright © 2001 Thankyou Music

YOU CAN HAVE MY WHOLE LIFE,
You can come and have it all:
I don't want to go my own way now,
I love to feel Your presence
And I know Your saving grace.
I am nothing when You are second place.

I've been born to give You praise,
Not to yearn and strive for worldly things.
I've been born to love Your ways,
Take my pride and let me always say:
I want to go Your way now.

1661 Martyn Layzell
Copyright © 2002 Thankyou Music

YOU CHOSE THE CROSS with every breath,
The perfect life, the perfect death:
You chose the cross.
A crown of thorns You wore for us,
And crowned us with eternal life:
You chose the cross.
And though Your soul was overwhelmed with
  pain,
Obedient to death You overcame.

I'm lost in wonder,
I'm lost in love,
I'm lost in praise forevermore.
Because of Jesus' unfailing love
I am forgiven, I am restored.

You loosed the cords of sinfulness
And broke the chains of my disgrace:
You chose the cross.
Up from the grave victorious,
You rose again so glorious:
You chose the cross.
The sorrow that surrounded You was mine,
'Yet not My will but Yours be done!' You
  cried.

1662 Matt Redman
Copyright © 1996 Thankyou Music

YOU CONFIDE IN THOSE WHO FEAR YOU,
Share the secrets of Your heart,
Friendship give to those who seek to
Honour You with every part.
Though I'm one of unclean lips, Lord,
I am crying 'Woe is me!'
Trying now to rid myself of
All the things that hinder me from...

Knowing You, hearing You speak,
Seeing You move mysteriously.
Your whisperings in my soul's ear:
I want the friendship and the fear
Of knowing You.

There is one thing You have spoken,
There are two things I have found:
You, O Lord, are ever loving,
You, O Lord, are always strong.
I am longing to discover
Both the closeness and the awe,
Feel the nearness of Your whisper,
Hear the glory of Your roar, just...

1663
Martyn Layzell
Copyright © 2002 Thankyou Music

YOU GAVE YOUR ONLY SON,
Came down from heaven above,
Endured the cross, so I might know
This love that reached for me,
A love that sets me free,
Your sacrifice has saved my soul.

Today I'm reminded of Your grace;
Always living now to sing Your praise,
Your praise.

Praise You, Jesus, I praise You,
I lift my hands and sing.
Embrace You, I will embrace You,
My Saviour and my King, my King.

I could not earn this love,
Such undeserved love;
Jesus, I know You are the way.
You paid the price for me,
Your blood was shed for me,
And in Your mercy took my place.

1664
Nathan & David Fellingham
Copyright © 1998 Thankyou Music

YOU HAVE GIVEN ME NEW LIFE;
Now my heart is satisfied.
I'm tasting the power of the age to come,
I'm living in the glory
Of the resurrected Son.
I'm walking in the light
And all that I now do is for You.

Pouring over me,
Everlasting love and mercy,
Over me in a flood of power.
Pouring over me, abounding grace so
free,
Over me Your unending love.

I've never had a friend like You;
All that You've promised You will do.
I'm drinking from the fountain
That will never run dry,
I'm living in the joy of a heart that's purified.
I'm walking now with You,
And all I have is Yours,
Take my life.

1665
Noel Richards
Copyright © 1999 Thankyou Music

YOU HAVE LAID YOUR HAND ON ME,
I am changed forever;
There is nothing that compares
With knowing You.
You have spoken words of love
That lift my Spirit higher;
Jesus Christ, my dearest friend,
I'm never letting go.

How can I live, how can I live,
How can I live without Your love?
How can I live, how can I live,
How can I live without Your love?

Help me never to forget
What I used to be,
Though the past that I regret
Is over now.
I will never be ashamed
Of calling You my friend.
I no longer hide from You,
I'm running to Your side.

All the riches I possess
Are meaningless to me;
Your love is the greatest gift,
The very air I breathe.

1666
Matt Redman
Copyright © 1999 Thankyou Music

YOU LED ME TO THE CROSS,
And I saw Your face of mercy
In that place of love.
You opened up my eyes
To believe Your sweet salvation,
Where I'd been so blind.
Now that I'm living in Your all-forgiving love
My every road leads to the cross.

Jesus, keep me near the cross,
I won't forget the love You've shown.
Saviour, teach me of the cross,
I won't forget the love,
I won't forget the love You've shown.

And there's an empty tomb,
That tells me of Your resurrection
And my life in You.
The stone lies rolled away,
Nothing but those folded grave clothes
Where Your body lay.
Now that I'm living as a risen child of God,
My every road leads to the cross.

1667 Gareth Robinson & Joannah Oyeniran
Copyright © 2001 Thankyou Music

YOU POUR OUT GRACE on the broken-
  hearted,
And You lift the hope of the weary soul,
And You stretch out Your hand
With Your loving mercy.
You saw this heart that was lost and broken,
And You felt the pain of my loneliness,
And You befriended me
And restored my dignity.

  You alone revealed the love of God to me,
  And You alone given everything for
    me;
  And You alone deserve the highest praise,
    Jesus.

You demonstrated the life of love to me,
And how it was that You wanted me to live:
Heart of compassion and hands of healing.
I need Your Spirit to help accomplish this:
Abundant grace and Your strength in
  weakness,
And the steady hand of the Father holding
  me.

And You have given me great salvation,
And You have given me hope eternal,
And every day I will look to give You
All the glory that's due Your name.

1668 Johnny Parks
Copyright © 2001 Thankyou Music

YOU'RE THE ONE WHO GAVE HIS SON,
Who will freely give us all things,
And nothing can be against us
God is still for us.
And all things work for good
For those who love the Lord,
And nothing can be against us
When You are still for us.

And we're convinced
That neither death nor life,
Angels or demons,
Height nor depths, nor what's to come
Can cut us off from the love of God.

  God is still for us, God is still for us,
  God is still for us, turn around.
  He is still for us, God is still for us,
  God is still for us, turn around.

When hardship or danger comes,
We know that God gave His only Son.
So as a body we are assured
That God is still for us.
We look to You, Lord,
We stand on Your word;
We're holding on
To the promise You've made –
That nothing can be against us
When You are still for us.

1669 Stuart Townend & Keith Getty
Copyright © 2002 Thankyou Music

YOU'RE THE WORD OF GOD THE FATHER,
From before the world began;
Every star and every planet
Has been fashioned by Your hand.
All creation holds together
By the power of Your voice:
Let the skies declare Your glory,
Let the land and seas rejoice!

  You're the Author of creation,
  You're the Lord of every man;
  And Your cry of love rings out
  Across the lands.

Yet You left the gaze of angels,
Came to seek and save the lost,
And exchanged the joy of heaven
For the anguish of a cross.
With a prayer You fed the hungry,
With a word You stilled the sea;
Yet how silently You suffered
That the guilty may go free.

With a shout You rose victorious,
Wresting victory from the grave,
And ascended into heaven
Leading captives in Your wake.
Now You stand before the Father
Interceding for Your own.
From each tribe and tongue and nation
You are leading sinners home.

1670 E.H. Plumptre (1821–91) adapt. Keith Getty
Copyright © 2001 Thankyou Music

YOUR HAND, O GOD, HAS GUIDED
Your church from age to age,
The tale of love is written
For us on every page.
Our fathers knew Your goodness,
And we Your works record,
And each of these bear witness:
One church, one faith, one Lord.

One church, one faith, one Lord of life,
One Father, one Spirit, one Christ.
One church, one faith, one Lord of life,
One heavenly King, Lord of all.

Your mercy never fails us,
Or leaves Your work undone;
With Your right hand to help us,
The victory shall be won.
And then with heaven's angels
Your name shall be adored,
And they shall praise You, singing:
One church, one faith, one Lord.

1671 James Gregory
Copyright © 2002 Thankyou Music

YOUR KINDNESS overwhelmed me,
The love that captured me.
You helped me to believe
That You delight in me.
You led me to the Father,
And introduced us there,
The Spirit poured out grace,
And filled me with Your praise.

> *You are wonderful, beautiful,*
> *Merciful, and all my life*
> *And my heart belongs to You.*
> (Repeat)

Your plans for me are greater
Than I had ever thought,
You're daily changing me,
Revealing more to me.
My love for You is growing,
And as I reach for You,
Your Spirit pours out grace
And fills me with Your praise.

1672 Darlene Zschech & David Moyse
Copyright © 2000 Darlene Zschech & David Moyse/
Hillsong Publishing/Kingsway Music

YOUR KINGDOM GENERATION
Declares Your majesty,
And our lives are resounding with Your
  praise.
We see Your Spirit moving,
We burn with holy fire.
Your glory is seen through all the earth.
You set eternity in my heart,
So I'll live for You, for You.

Hallelujah, hallelujah,
Honour and praise forever.
We'll shout a victory cry from here
To eternity.
Hallelujah, hallelujah,
We'll take our place in history.
We'll shout Your awesome love from here
To eternity.

1673 Reuben Morgan
Copyright © 1998 Reuben Morgan/
Hillsong Publishing/Kingsway Music

YOUR LIGHT broke through my night,
Restored exceeding joy.
Your grace fell like the rain,
And made this desert live.

> *You have turned*
> *My mourning into dancing.*
> *You have turned*
> *My sorrow into joy.*

Your hand lifted me up,
I stand on higher ground.
Your praise rose in my heart,
And made this valley sing.

This is how we overcome. *(×6)*

> *You turned...*

1674 Stuart Townend
Copyright © 1999 Thankyou Music

YOUR LOVE, shining like the sun,
Pouring like the rain,
Raging like the storm,
Refreshing me again.
I receive Your love.

Your grace frees me from the past,
It purges every sin,
It purifies my heart
And heals me from within.
I receive Your grace.

> *Pour over me,*
> *Pour over me,*
> *Let Your rain flood this thirsty soul.*
> *Pour over me Your waves of love,*
> *Pour over me.*

I come and lay my burden down
Gladly at Your feet,
I'm opening up my heart;
Come make this joy complete.
I receive Your peace.

1675 Chris Tomlin, Jesse Reeves & Louie Giglio
Copyright © 1999 worshiptogether.com songs/
Adm. by Kingsway Music

YOUR LOVE HAS CAPTURED ME,
Your grace has set me free;
Your life, the air I breathe:
Be glorified in me.

You set my feet to dancing,
You set my heart on fire,
In the presence of a thousand kings
You are my one desire.
And I stand before You now
With trembling hands lifted high,
Be glorified.

1676 Brenton Brown & Brian Doerksen
Copyright © 2000 Vineyard Songs (UK/Eire)/
Adm. by CopyCare

YOUR LOVE IS AMAZING,
Steady and unchanging;
Your love is a mountain,
Firm beneath my feet.
Your love is a mystery,
How You gently lift me;
When I am surrounded,
Your love carries me.

Hallelujah, hallelujah,
Hallelujah, Your love makes me sing.
Hallelujah, hallelujah,
Hallelujah, Your love makes me sing.

Your love is surprising,
I can feel it rising,
All the joy that's growing
Deep inside of me.
Every time I see You,
All Your goodness shines through,
And I can feel this God song
Rising up in me.

1677 Robert Critchley
Copyright © 2000 Thankyou Music

YOUR LOVE IS BETTER THAN WINE,
Your name like sweetest perfume;
Oh, that You would kiss me
With the kisses of Your mouth
And draw me, draw me after You.
I hear You whisper my name,
And like a moth to the flame
I fly into the fire of Your intimate love
As You draw me, draw me after You.

Draw me after You, (×3)
And let us run together.
(Repeat)

Jesus You're the One, (×3)
That I will love forever.
Jesus You're the One, (×3)
That I will love forevermore.

So amazing, so divine,
I am Yours and You are mine.
For such love there are no words,
'Cause loving You is heaven on earth.

1678 Greg Shepherd
Copyright © 2000 Thankyou Music

YOUR NAME IS LOVE,
The love that went to the cross.
Your name is peace,
You've taken my sins away,
And how I love all that You are,
Your name is Jesus.

Your name is truth,
The truth that sets me free.
Your name is hope,
Hope for eternity,
And how I love all that You are,
Your name is Jesus.

Jesus, Name above all names,
I will ever more proclaim:
'Worthy is the Lamb
To receive all power,
To receive all praise.'

Your name is Lord,
I gladly bow the knee.
You are a friend,
A friend of sinners like me,
And how I love all that You are,
Your name is Jesus.

1679 Dave Bilbrough
Copyright © 2002 Thankyou Music

YOURS IS THE KINGDOM,
The power and the glory,
Forever and ever,
Forever and ever, Amen!
(Repeat)

A trumpet blast will herald
The day of Your return:
Your glory and Your splendour
Will be seen in all the earth!

And oh, what a day,
Oh, what a day that will be,
When the earth joins with heaven
In worship and praise to Jesus!

The time is drawing nearer,
I believe it's coming soon,
When we will rise to greet You
As a bride to meet her groom.

1680 Vicky Beeching
Copyright © 2001 Vineyard Songs (UK/Eire)/
Adm. by CopyCare

YOUR VOICE is the voice that
Commanded the universe to be.
Your voice is the voice that
Is speaking words of love to me:
How can it be?

Awesome God, holy God,
I worship You in wonder.
Awesome God, holy God,
As You draw near I'm humbled
By Your majesty, and the mystery
Of Your great love for me.

Your arms are the arms that
Hung shining stars in deepest space.
Your arms are the arms that
Surround me in a warm embrace:
Amazing grace.

1681 Brian Houston
Copyright © 2000 Thankyou Music

YOUR WHISPER TO MY SOUL
When I was like a child,
Lifted off the yoke,
Planted fields of hope
In this heart of mine.
You took me as I am,
You knew what I had done,
Still You took my shame,
And You called my name,
I was overcome.

When You broke the bonds
Of how I used to be,
You rolled away the stone,
You set the captive free.

I wanna thank You,
You're the God of mercy;
I wanna thank You, Lord,
For giving me peace.
I wanna thank You,
You're the God who loved me;
I wanna thank You,
You're the God who rescued me.

You covered all my sin,
Restored to me my youth again.
And I am satisfied,
For You have healed me
And redeemed me,
Crowned my head with endless beauty,
Endless beauty.

1682 Reuben Morgan
Copyright © 1998 Reuben Morgan/
Hillsong Publishing/Kingsway Music

YOU SAID:
'Ask and you will receive
Whatever you need.'
You said:
'Pray, and I'll hear from heaven,
And I'll heal your land.'

You said
Your glory will fill the earth,
Like water the sea.
You said:
'Lift up your eyes,
The harvest is here,
The kingdom is here.'

You said:
'Ask, and I'll give the nations to you.'
O Lord, that's the cry of my heart.
Distant shores and the islands will see
Your light as it rises on us.

O Lord, I ask for the nations.

1683 Paul Ewing
Copyright © 2000 Paul Ewing/
Hillsong Publishing/Kingsway Music

YOU SET ME APART,
Gave me a new heart,
Filled with compassion
To share Your great love.
Show me Your ways,
I want to know You.
Guide me in truth,
My hope is in You.

That I may dwell in Your house forever,
Lifting up Your name;
Dwell in Your house forevermore.
(Repeat)

I'll hold on to You,
My strength and my refuge.
Whom shall I fear?
I know You are near.
All of my days
I live for You, Lord.
Establish my path,
There's one thing I ask.

Holy Spirit, have Your way.
Sweet anointing, teach our hearts,
Our lives, we pray.

1684   Tim Hughes
Copyright © 2001 Thankyou Music

YOU SHAPED THE HEAVENS and the earth,
Revealed Your splendour.
You spoke Your life into our hearts,
So we belong to You.

> *You are the Maker of all things,*
> *First and the Last;*
> *Creation sings praise to You, God.*
> *You're reigning in glory,*
> *Ancient of Days;*
> *Your people sing praise to You, God.*

Creator God, in You all things
Now hold together,
Working Your wonders day by day,
You'll reign forever.

And earth joins with heaven
Declaring Your glory;
Proclaiming the works of Your hands.
(Repeat)

1685   Matt Redman & Chris Tomlin
Copyright © 2002 worshiptogether.com songs/
Six Steps Music/Thankyou Music/
Adm. by Kingsway Music

YOU SPREAD OUT THE SKIES
Over empty space,
Said 'Let there be light' –
To a dark and formless world
Your light was born.

You spread out Your arms
Over empty hearts,
Said 'Let there be light' –
To a dark and hopeless world
Your Son was born.

You made the world and saw that it was
good,
You sent Your only Son, for You are good.

> *What a wonderful Maker,*
> *What a wonderful Saviour.*
> *How majestic Your whispers,*
> *And how humble Your love.*
> *With a strength like no other,*
> *And the heart of a Father,*
> *How majestic Your whispers,*
> *What a wonderful God.*

No eye has fully seen
How beautiful the cross,
And we have only heard
The faintest whisper of
How great You are.

1686   Dave Bilbrough
Copyright © 2000 Thankyou Music

YOU TAKE ME BY THE HAND,
And though there are times I don't
    understand,
Your love will never fail
And my heart belongs to You.
Even when the rain clouds break
And the cold wind blows all around me,
I will not be put to shame;
Lord, my hope is in Your name.
You will carry me on Your shoulders
And lead me home.

Carry me over troubled waters,
Carry me over stormy seas.
When the skies are dark and heavy,
By Your grace You'll carry me.
Though the way can seem uncertain
Because the time of change has come,
You will carry me on Your shoulders
And lead me home.

1687   Stuart Townend
Copyright © 1999 Thankyou Music

YOU'VE PLACED A HUNGER IN MY HEART
To see Your glory,
You've caused a thirst that I cannot ignore;
You've stirred a passion that will
Drive me to Your presence,
And I won't rest until
You've heard me cry for more.

> *Come as a mighty torrent,*
> *Come as a raging fire,*
> *Come as a hurricane that drives*
> *The heat of my desire.*
> *Come in the smallest whisper,*
> *Come as the quiet dew:*
> *We don't care how You come,*
> *As long as You come to us.*

Though people mock the church
And curse the One who made them,
Your kingdom is advancing every day;
Like living stones we're being
Built into a temple,
We've seen the glory
And we cannot turn away.

Is this the summer that will
See a mighty harvest?
A sense of expectation fills the air;
Though sin abounds,
Your love is streaming to the nations,
Let mercy triumph
Over judgement everywhere.

Come to the politician,
Come to the refugee,
Come to the victim of respectable society;
Come to the mighty fallen,
Come to the poor oppressed:
We don't care how You come,
As long as You come to them.

1688 Lara Martin (Abundant Life Ministries,
Bradford, England)
Copyright © 2002 Thankyou Music

YOU'VE PLACED A SONG WITHIN MY HEART,
And this song will bless You,
Your praise is always on my lips.
Whatever life may bring,
I know that You are God;
So I can trust in You and sing.

Immanuel, God with us,
Immanuel, You are near.
Immanuel, my God is for me,
My God is for me.
So...

I will bless the Lord at all times,
I will bless the Lord at all times.
In every situation I will give You praise,
I will rejoice in You always.
(Repeat)

1689 Matt Redman
Copyright © 2000 Thankyou Music

YOU'VE PUT A NEW SONG IN MY MOUTH;
It is a hymn of praise to You.
Justice and mercy are its theme,
And I will live it back to You.

The kind of fast You've chosen, Lord,
It must reach out
To broken lives and to the poor:
So change me, Lord.

I know You are the orphan's hope,
I know You are the widow's song;
You're Father where no father lives,
And to the lonely You're a friend.
O Lord, You're showing me what's on Your
    heart.

Lord, I won't bring an empty song;
It's meaningless
Without compassion in my life,
And holiness.

1690 Neil Bennetts
Copyright © 2002 Thankyou Music

YOU'VE TOUCHED MY HEART
With words of Your mercy
And thoughts of Your beauty.
Your presence, God,
Has captured me now
With the hope of Your glory.
You've opened my eyes to see
You're all that this heart can need.

For what is worthy of the King of kings,
But a heart that is satisfied in loving You
Yours is the song,
Yours is the praise I'll bring,
With a passion for the wonder
Of seeing Your glory here.

This song I'll bring
Is my song of love from
A heart that's been broken.
It's what You've done,
For I've been set free by
The life that You've given.
Faithful and holy One,
Forever I live to sing.

Addresses for Copyright and Information

Company names are under first name or word. Individuals' names are listed under surname.

Ambushed Ltd, 5–9 Surrey Street, Croydon, CR0 1RG, UK.
email: info@follysend.org
website: www.follysend.org
Ateliers et Presses de Taizé, F-71250 Taizé-Communauté, France.
email: community@taize.fr
Barrie, Karen, 511 Maple Ave., Wilmette, Illinois 60091, USA.
Barthow, Mary R., 15 Aunceston Rise, Alfriston, South Auckland, New Zealand.
Behrns, Gary, 2406 Colonial Hills Road, Jefferson City, MO 65109, USA.
Bucks Music Ltd, Onward House, 11 Uxbridge Street, London, W8 7TQ, UK. *(Rights administered in the UK & Republic of Ireland.)*
Central Board of Finance of the Church of England (The), Church House, Great Smith Street, London, SW1P 3NZ, UK.
email: copyright@c-of-e.org.uk
Chance, Kay, Dr. H.-Jasper-Str. 20, D-37581 Bad Gandersheim, Germany.
CopyCare, P.O. Box 77, Hailsham, East Sussex, BN27 3EF, UK.
email: music@copycare.com
Curious? Music UK, P.O. Box 40, Arundel, BN18 0UQ, UK.
email: info@furiousrecords.co.uk
Daniel L. Schutte & New Dawn Music, 5536 North East Hassalo, Portland, OR 97213, USA.
David Higham Associates Ltd, 5–8 Lower John Street, Golden Square, London, W1R 3PE, UK.
Daybreak Music Ltd, P.O. Box 2848, Eastbourne, BN20 7XP, UK.
email: info@daybreakmusic.co.uk
Dudley-Smith, Timothy, 9 Ashlands, Ford, Salisbury, SP4 6DY, UK. *(For Europe, incl. UK & Ireland, and in all territories not controlled by Hope Publishing Company.)*
GIA Publications Inc., 7404 South Mason Avenue, Chicago, IL 60638, USA.
website: www.giamusic.com
Gabriel Music Inc., P.O. Box 840999, Houston, Texas 77284-0999, USA.
Gordon V. Thompson, a division of Warner Chappell Music Canada Ltd, 40 Sheppard Avenue West, Suite 800, Toronto, Ontario, M2N 6K9, Canada.
Grace! Music, 11610 Grandview Road, Kansas City, MO 64137, USA.
Heart of David Music, 14815 Pineview Drive, Grandview, MO 64030, USA.
High-Fye Music Ltd, 8–9 Frith Street, London, W1D 3JB, UK. *(Used by permission of Music Sales Ltd.)*
IQ Music Ltd, Commercial House, 52 Perrymount Road, Haywards Heath, West Sussex, RH16 3DT, UK. *(For the world.)*
email: iq.music@virgin.net
ICG, P.O. Box 24149, Nashville, TN 37202, USA.

Josef Weinberger Ltd, 12–14 Mortimer Street, London, W1N 7RD, UK.
Jubilate Hymns Ltd, Southwick House, 4 Thorne Park Road, Chelston, Torquay, TQ2 6RX, UK.
email: jubilatemw@aol.com
King, Mary Lou, 7013 E. Keynote, Longbeach, CA 90808, USA.
Kingdom Faith Ministries, Foundry Lane, Horsham, West Sussex, RH13 5PX, UK.
Kingsway Music, P.O. Box 75, Eastbourne, East Sussex, BN23 6NW, UK.
email: tym@kingsway.co.uk
Lea, Melva, Larry Lea Ministries, P.O. Box 1102, Sherman, TX75091-1102, USA.
Len Magee Music, P.O. Box 6327, South Tweed Heads, NSW 2486, Australia.
MCA Music Publishing, 2440 Sepulveda Blvd Suite 100, Los Angeles, CA 90064-1712, USA. *(Used by permission of Music Sales Ltd.)*
Make Way Music, P.O. Box 263, Croydon, Surrey, CR9 5AP, UK.
email: info@makewaymusic.com
McIntosh, Mike & Claire, P.O. Box 24000, Federal Way, WA 98093, USA.
OCP Publications, 5536 N.E. Hassalo, Portland, OR 97213, USA.
OMF International, Station Approach, Borough Green, Sevenoaks, TN15 8BG, UK.
Oxford University Press, Great Clarendon Street, Oxford, OX2 6DP, UK.
PolyGram Music Publishing Ltd, 47 British Grove, London W4, UK. *(Used by permission of Music Sales Ltd.)*
Signalgrade Ltd, 48 Chatsworth Avenue, London, SW20 8JZ, UK.
Simmonds, Clive, 22 St Michaels Road, Bedford, MK40 2LT, UK.
Smail, Mary, 151 Elm Park, London, SW2 2EE, UK.
Sound III, Elisnore House, 77 Fulham Palace Road, London, W6 8JA, UK. *(Used by permission of Music Sales Ltd.)*
Sovereign Lifestyle Music, P.O. Box 356, Leighton Buzzard, LU7 3WP, UK.
email: sovereignm@aol.com
Sovereign Music UK, P.O. Box 356, Leighton Buzzard, LU7 3WP, UK.
email: sovereignm@aol.com
Stassen, Linda, 175 Heggie Lane, Erin, TN 37061, USA.
TKO Publishing, P.O. Box 130, Hove, East Sussex, BN3 6QU.
Thankyou Music *(Adm. by worshiptogether.com songs excl. UK & Europe, adm. by Kingsway Music.)* See Kingsway Music.
WGRG (Wild Goose Resource Group), Iona Community, Fourth Floor, Savoy House, 140 Sauchiehall Street, Glasgow, G2 3DH.
World Wide Worship, Buxhall, Stowmarket, Suffolk, IP14 3BW, UK. *(For the UK & European territory only.)*

Index of titles and first lines

(Titles where different from first lines are shown in *italics*)